WHILE PARIS LAUGHED

LEONARD MERRICK

WHILE
PARIS LAUGHED

Being Pranks and Passions of
The Poet Tricotrin

BY

LEONARD MERRICK

AUTHOR OF "CONRAD IN QUEST OF HIS YOUTH," "THE MAN WHO
UNDERSTOOD WOMEN," ETC.

NEW YORK
E. P. DUTTON AND COMPANY
681 FIFTH AVENUE

Printed in the United States of America

CONTENTS

WHILE PARIS LAUGHED

WHILE PARIS LAUGHED

I

"On Est Mieux Ici Qu'en Face"

ON the quai de Passy, in Paris, stands an unattractive little café with a witty window.
A faded announcement in the language of the land
informs the observant that "One is Better Off in
Here than Opposite." And when one glances
opposite, the alternative is—the river.

Without a premonition that he was to discover
this humble café, so remote from his lodging off
the avenue du Maine, monsieur Xavier Mariquot,
on an evening of his twenty-fourth summer, bade
farewell to the world.

On the table, explaining the motives for his
suicide, lay an epistle that he had been revising
for some hours. It was directed to a friend, but
as Mariquot was an aspiring poet, it was intended
primarily for the Press. Now that it was finished
and sealed, the cheerfulness induced by its composition deserted him; he reflected wistfully that
he himself would never see his pathetic letter in
print, and regretted that it could not appear be-

11

fore he died. He wondered whether the public
would do justice to his metaphors. Also, he wondered whether the news would be headed "Suicide
Of A Poet," or "Lovers Drown Together." He
hoped for the former.

The artistry of Mariquot had moved him to
make such a host of alterations in the letter before
the fair copy was finally accomplished that the
floor was strewn with the rough drafts. He col-
lected these, and, having burnt them carefully—
all of us would wish our letter on the brink of
suicide to be regarded as spontaneous—took his
hat from the accustomed peg.

"For the last time!" said the youth thoughtfully. He cast a backward glance at the room
and slammed the door.

A full moon shone over Montparnasse, and life
did not look repellent to him. He couldn't avoid
remembering that this double tragedy had been
the suggestion of the lady whom he was walking
very slowly to meet, and that when he dramatically agreed to it he had, so to speak, been
"rushed." Originally it had been her Southern
temperament, plus her Southern beauty, that en-
slaved him, but at that time he had not foreseen
his father wrenching him from Poetry and Paris
and convulsing two kindred souls. In view of his
implacable parent, perhaps a gramme or two less
temperament in the lady might have made for
good? To be sure, a career of commerce in Rennes
would have been disgusting, but the river would

be very deep. And he was touchingly young to die.

Well, all Paris would say as much when they read his letter in the newspapers! The reflection encouraged him. "So young! Poor boy!" Boulevardiers would shake their heads compassionately over their apéritifs; lovely women would utter his name in salons: "Xavier Mariquot, evidently a genius, gone to his grave!" Yes, he was going to create a sensation at last! . . . Still, he wouldn't be here to enjoy it. "There's always something!" sighed Mariquot, glowering at the heavens.

She was waiting for him by the Bullier-Nouveau. She wore a simple frock of black, and though she usually affected hats with a sweeping brim, had donned a toque for this occasion. She was on the stage—when she got engagements— and realised the kind of garments becoming to a heroine on the road to drown. In the glitter of the entrance, to which happier couples were hastening, with their pumps wrapped in copies of *La Patrie,* her oval face was very pale; there was perhaps a tinge of indecision in her sombre eyes. She slipped her arm through his without speaking, and he said politely: "I hope I am not late?"

His affinity shook her head, and they turned slowly to the boulevard St-Michel.

"Enfin, the night has come, Xavier!" she said in contralto tones.

"It has come!" echoed the youth in the bass.

"We have danced our last measure in there, you and I." And, with a transition to the minor, he continued: "Do you recall our first polka, Delphine, the evening that we first met? It was a wet Saturday——"

"A Thursday," she murmured, "a gala night—the Thursday before the Réveillon."

"I think it was a Saturday," he dissented, "because I remember vividly that I had gone to be shaved late in the afternoon, with the idea of making it do for the morrow as well and saving a copper or two. I remember, also, how dull I had found the ball, and that I had intended to say sarcastically, in leaving: 'Le Bullier-Nouveau,' you call it? You should call it 'Le Bullier-Mort!' And then my path crossed yours, and epigrams were forgotten, and coppers were as naught."

"How it comes back to me!" she said pensively. "You were standing by the punching-machine. Is it not strange how a woman's instinct prognosticates? Mysteriously, I knew that Fate did not mean us to be strangers long."

"To me it seemed that Fate would forbid me ever to address you. How haughty you looked—so disdainful! Nine times I meandered round, to beg you for a dance, before I found the pluck to say a syllable."

"I began to think you must be a foreigner who knew no French. And then the bouquetière came by with her basket—do you remember?—and you

stuttered: 'Do you like violets, mademoiselle?'
And next it was cherry-brandy, and next it was
the polka—and next it was our love. Oh, Xavier,
if the bouquetière had not come by with her basket,
we might not now be on our way to die!''

"Do you regret?" demanded Mariquot, kindling
with hope.

"For myself, no!" she affirmed. "What could
existence yield to me if we were parted? But to
you? I have wondered in harassed moments
whether the years might not bring happiness to
you?" Her clasp on his arm tightened eagerly.
"I would not be selfish, Sweet Ideal. It is all your
bright young future I am aiding you to sacrifice,
all the glorious promise of your flowering man-
hood. If time could teach you to forget me in my
wretchedness, to find joy without me, I would
steel myself, even now, to bear the martyrdom of
life alone.''

"The way you put it amounts to asking me
whether I have been deceiving myself all along,"
objected Mariquot. "Am I a ridiculous boy, to
mistake a passing fancy for the great passion of
a lifetime? Have my vows been bosh? Is my
masterpiece pickles—the epic of my devotion for
you, throb by throb, from that first Saturday, or
Thursday, whichever it was? No, Delphine, I
cannot subscribe to that! Yet," he went on
persuasively, "there is this to be said. To *you*
time might grant compensations which would be
denied to *me*. To me it could afford nothing save

a comfortable salary from a permanent source—
by degrees, a solid income, a cosy appartement in
a pleasant quarter, a sound bordeaux with my
dinner. What are such things worth? Are you
aiding me to sacrifice anything for which you
might be severely censured—for which you might
reproach yourself bitterly, if age had endowed
you with more wisdom and self-control? But to
yourself! Who shall say to what effulgent heights
your beauty and your histrionic powers might not
elevate you? I can see you crowned with laurels,
if you are but patient to endure a while. I see
you reigning at the Français! I see you gliding
through the Arc de Triomphe in your car! I see
these sights with thrilling clearness. My adoration
must not blind me to my duty. If you could be
strong to wait for laurels without me, I would
even now be man enough to submit to the Philistine plenty that my father offers in Rennes."

The hand upon his coat-sleeve trembled somewhat. There was a brief pause. Then she returned a shade sullenly:

"In plain French, you suggest that *I* have been
making a mountain out of a molehill. You ask
me whether my resolve to drown myself was anything more serious than a fit of hysterics! I am
no more a sentimental idiot than *you* are!"

Their progress for some distance was made
silently, if one omits to count Mariquot's groan.
Each contemplated the climax with increased dis-

affection, but each felt the loophole indicated by
the other to be undignified.

With relief, they noted that the quays were not
deserted at this early hour, and they wandered
aimlessly along the boulevard du Palais. On the
pont au Change the girl suddenly halted—her face
upturned, then bowed.

"Not here!" panted Mariquot. "What are
you thinking about? Look at the people!"

"I am only fancying," she told him. "How
the Seine calls to me—how it calls, Xavier! Look
down, beloved! Below the quiver there is peace."

"Peace!" concurred Mariquot, clenching his
teeth to stop their chattering.

"One plunge together, and then—oblivion!"

"You will suffer first, my own," he muttered.
"You will flounder frightfully."

"You also," she darted; "your tortures will
be atrocious. Yes, it will be excruciating for both
of us. You will be a green and repulsive object
when we are found. Yet, speaking for myself,
better death together than life apart! You feel
that, too, Xavier?"

"Do I feel it?" stammered Mariquot. "Do
I feel it?" No adequate answer presenting itself,
he repeated impressively, "Do I feel it? . . . If
I bewail anything, other than your loss of the
triumphant future that you might know, it is
just this," he added: "Paris may not understand
how violently I reciprocated your devotion—people may not grasp the true inwardness of my

tragedy. The fact is, that in the few Last Words
that I have scribbled to a comrade, I touched upon
the detail that the publishers have rejected all my
work. If, by a fatal mischance, the letter should
be profaned by print, it may lead shallow thinkers
to regard me as a despairing poet rather than as
an anguished lover. I know how proud you are—
it is poignant to me to reflect that, after you have
cast away your exquisite young life solely because
I am all in all to you, the world may fail to realise
that *you* were all in all to *me*. I writhe in recognising that multitudes may say you bestowed a
more single-hearted passion than you aroused."
Again he regarded her expectantly. "I do not
even disguise from myself that you have the right
to resent my alluding to my literary ambitions
with what may be termed my last breath. No, I
do not deny it! Your indignation would be justified. You are entitled perhaps to declare that I
have slighted you, to pronounce me unworthy of
the splendid sacrifice that you are about to make
for me!"

Delphine frowned darkly; her displeasure was
plain, and some seconds passed, in which encouragement held him breathless.

"My king," she said at last tartly, "the grandeur of your soul compels me to admit a similar slip
on my part. I, too, have scribbled a few Last
Words, and by some wandering impulse I referred
to the managers having overlooked my abilities
as an actress. If, by any abominable indiscretion,

the letter gets into the papers, it may appear that
my suicide was due to my professional afflictions
rather than to my idolatry of *you!* Your self-
respect is more precious to me than my own—my
blunder wrings my heart when I reflect that, after
you are green and ghastly, everybody may conclude that you were incapable of inspiring a love
as absorbing as you gave. In my turn, I am open
to reproaches! In my turn, I am defenceless if
you proclaim me to be unworthy of your death!''

Mariquot had listened to this rejoinder in profound despondence. Twice he had opened his
mouth to interrupt her; and when he spoke, his
voice had distinctly an angry ring:

"Look here, if you figure yourself that *I* am
going to be the first to back out, you are vastly
mistaken!" he exclaimed. "I am every bit as
keen on dying as I was when I consented to it.''

"If you imagine that *I* am going to sing small
first, you had better think again!" retorted the
girl scornfully. "It would take more than a drop
into the Seine to make *me* look a fool. If you
don't want to back out, why do you keep talking
about it so much? *I'm* ready.''

"Well, suppose we get a move on us, then?"
he said, with a scowl.

They lagged from the bridge glumly, arm in
arm no longer, and their eyes averted from each
other. Viewing the lights of the Théâtre Sarah-
Bernhardt, Mariquot was reminded of a performance that he had witnessed there, with an order,

in blither days, and he reflected that suicides, in relation to one's self, were less gorgeously gratifying than in the works of the dramatists. Delphine's gaze dwelt upon the lamps of the Châtelet, and memory reanimated an engagement, agreeable, if undistinguished, that she had once fulfilled on its stage as a fairy. Now she could not aspire to become even a fairy again!

The quai de la Mégisserie was also populous:

"Peste!—more people!" cried Mariquot. "We should certainly be rescued. What a misfortune that the moon is shining!"

"I much fear," she responded, "that we shall be obliged to wait a long time. See, couples everywhere! It would have been less wearisome if you had made a later appointment."

"I had no private intimation that all the idiots of the quartier were to select the quays to spoon on this evening," he growled. "We should find it lonelier much further on. Would it fatigue you to walk?"

"Probably," she said. "But we shall have a long rest!"

Their promenade offered few distractions. By the time they had trudged as far as the quai de Passy the lovers paused simultaneously. The coincidence occurred in the glimmer of a café window, and Mariquot remarked, with a dry mouth: "Do you know, I am inclined to think that we might enter this place? Providentially I have a franc on me. We can make our consommations last till all is quiet enough for us to do the deed."

"You may be right," Delphine acknowledged. "Our last glass together. So be it!"

The little café boasted no more than one other customer—a young man who sat writing ardently, an intellectual brow supported by a restless hand. The shade of his luxuriant locks commended itself to Delphine's attention almost before she had drunk half her beer at a draught, and when, in moments, he raised his head to seek inspiration of the ceiling, the melancholy countenance that he displayed was so engaging that she would have welcomed a continuous view.

Meanwhile Mariquot had been prompted to contemplate the last franc that he was ever to finger, and as he did so disquietude assailed him. The franc was bad.

"Have you, by chance, any cash in your purse, Delphine?" he inquired.

"I have no purse either," she said. "I left it carefully in my lodging, directed to my family. Why should I drown with purses in my pocket?"

"I made the same reflection myself. Well, the only coin that I did bring is a wrong 'un, and we have drunk the best part of our bocks! I foresee trouble.'

Unwittingly he had drawn the waiter's eye to them, and when their impecuniosity was manifest, the trouble became acute. At this juncture the young man, who, having finished his letter, was observing the discussion, rose and approached

them. Casting a five-franc piece upon the table
with a courtly air, he said: "Permit me to come to
the rescue, I pray you, monsieur!"

"Oh, monsieur!" ejaculated Mariquot, embarrassed. "It is princely, it is unparalleled! But,
at the same time——"

"You need feel no hesitation," insisted the
stranger. "To me the coin is valueless, for I am
at the point of leaving France."

"There are always money-changers," mentioned Mariquot.

"In the Land for which *I* am bound," returned
the other, with a dreamy smile, "there is neither
money-changer nor money."

"Oh, mon Dieu!" gasped Mariquot, jumping.
"What, you, too?"

In the breathless instant succeeding this double
revelation, which held three customers spell-
bound, the waiter picked up the five-franc piece.

" '*Too,*' you said!" murmured the young man,
finding his voice at last. "So you and I are fel-
low-travellers, monsieur? And—and madame?"

"Madame is leaving with me."

"You are blessed." His protracted glance at
Delphine proclaimed it no empty compliment. "*I*
go loveless and alone." With a deep sigh, he continued: "My few Last Words have just been
scribbled, and I have nothing to do until I drown
myself at twelve o'clock. May I beg you to join
me in a bottle with the change? Waiter, the wine-
list!"

The pathos of his situation stirred Delphine deeply, and she broke in now: "But, monsieur, cannot we induce you to revoke your rash resolve? Do not think me presumptuous, but might not our counsel serve you in this crisis? So young!" she whispered to Mariquot.

"He is no younger than I am," said Mariquot shortly.

"Alas! I have already pondered the matter in all its bearings, madame," replied the other boy, with folded arms. "My resolution is inexorable, and at midnight there will be in Paris one poet less."

"'Poet,' did you say?" gibbered Mariquot, aghast.

"Yes, monsieur. I am called Gustave Tricotrin. To-night the name is not significant, but it is soon to figure largely in the papers!"

Mariquot's blood ran cold. What if his own drowned body should be fished out later than this chap's? His own effect would be crushingly discounted. How much sensation could then be hoped for? "Another Poet Commits Suicide"— he would be "another," an anti-climax, a plagiarist! . . . Death was robbed of its one grace.

"Nevertheless your compassion is sweet to me," admitted monsieur Tricotrin. "And if it will distract your minds from your calamities, I shall be honoured to confide my own." Without awaiting an affirmative, which he obviously took for granted, he continued: "Do not assume that

the purblind editors have spurred me to this pass,
for editors, I defy! It is Woman who has laid my
career in ruins.''

"A 'plagiarist'!'' moaned Mariquot vacantly.

"You said, monsieur?''

"Nothing,'' explained Mariquot, with a start.
"I was but soliloquising. Pray resume!''

"Though of noble descent, and dowered with
great gifts,'' monsieur Tricotrin resumed, "I
have never possessed a safety razor; and if you
are acquainted with the literary world, monsieur,
you may be aware that the alternative of resorting
to a barber is often a strain on the Budget. For
this reason, it was my custom to betake myself
to the cheapest rotter revealed to me—until one
fatal day. Accident forced me to enter an establishment above my means, and—I assure you,
madame—never should I have patronised it again
but that, in the mirror, I beheld the reflection of a
woman's face! She sat enthroned behind me, taking the money. She was the widow of the late
coiffeur.''

"So attractive?'' inquired Delphine, with a
strange pang at her heart.

"Ah, madame! And the way her hair was
done! Her beauty was, if I may say so, of a type
similar to your own. On the morrow, too, I
weakly went there, waiting till the desired chair
was vacant. Daily I squandered ten sous for the
exquisite pain of viewing her in the glass. She
marked my homage; she fostered it. She sold to

me combs and pomatums that I never used; I paid
for perfumes which I presented after purchase.
To prolong the perfect vision in the mirror, I was
shampooed, and singed, and frizzed. Finally I
was shaved twice a day, and she accepted my es-
cort to the Odéon."

"And when you owned you loved her?" asked
Delphine,

"She gave me hope. 'Twas all she gave. She
feigned to regard her bereavement as too recent
to allow decision. For months she has sported with
my worship. My life has been passed in her establishment! With the solitary exception of hair-
cutting, there is not a process practised in the
place to which I have not submitted myself *ad in-
finitum.* Enfin, she has wedded the head assistant
—and when I sobbed 'Coquette!' she derided me
with 'Client!' "

To this harangue Mariquot had paid no attention whatever, his abstraction passing unobserved
owing to the sympathetic interest yielded by Delphine. His brains were racked for a pretext to
elude the watery grave, which no longer guaran-
teed him posthumous distinction, and scarcely had
she set appreciative lips to the burgundy that had
been placed before them, than he leapt to his feet.

"Come!" he exclaimed, with a gesture of un-
controllable despair. "Monsieur, I entreat you
to excuse us—it is time we died."

"Why, what are you talking about?" faltered Delphine, dismayed. "It is nothing like late enough yet!"

"It is thoroughly late enough; it is the ideal hour. I can curb my impatience no longer. Come!" he persisted.

"But it is crazy!" Her voice was vexed. "We enter here to wait for the middle of the night, and we are no sooner comfortable than you want to go!"

"Do you refuse?" he demanded, reeling.

"I refuse to do any more stumping about the quays too soon," she said. "Sit down and be mannerly; what will monsieur Tricotrin think of you?"

"A—ah!" cried Mariquot. "It is for *him* you fain would linger; it is *his* companionship that makes you craven? Oh, Heaven! Maybe that 'woman's instinct' of yours 'prognosticates' again?"

"Monsieur"—Tricotrin rose superbly—"it appears to me that you are insolent. I should indulge myself by sending you my second, but the mutual circumstances forbid an appointment."

"False girl!" pursued Mariquot, disregarding the interruption. "You jilt me on the brink of the tomb. And is it for one so fickle that Xavier Mariquot would perish? Ah, no, my dignity restrains me! Though Lethe were sweet, my pride protests. I shall bear the burden of life. Better had I died before your perfidy was known! Farewell for ever!" And, upsetting a chair in his haste, he was gone and skipping along the pavement before Delphine or Tricotrin could utter so much as another word.

Their eyes met widely. A physiognomist might have said that relief lightened the mood of both.

"He was looking for a 'way out,' that's all," she said with a laugh. "It wasn't that he was really jealous."

"Could I aspire to dream otherwise? I should be vainglorious, indeed!" returned the host. In a tone of profound solicitude, he went on: "And you will be brave to rally from the blow of his unworthiness, will you not? I hope with all my broken heart you do not mean to waste your death, as well as your life on him, madame?"

" 'Mademoiselle'!" she murmured shyly.

"Let me prevail upon you to take your wine," said Tricotrin, drawing nearer. . . . "It is cosy here?"

"Yet there is a skeleton at the feast," repined Delphine.

"You think of hours gone beyond recall?"

"I think of the next hour to strike," she owned. "The skeleton that I see is yours."

"Can it be possible?" cried the boy, moved. "You feel for me so deeply, Child?" He drew nearer still. "Ah, if I had been granted your influence earlier, I should have been a happier man!"

Five minutes afterwards, when her influence had matured and his arms encircled her: "Is it not mysterious?'' he exclaimed devoutly. ''All the time, even while I traced my Last Words, something has seemed to insist that I should not die!''

Her tranquil gaze deciphered a sign backwards on the window.

''How true!'' breathed the young girl, in the harbour of her new friend's embrace. '' 'One is Better Off in Here than Opposite'!''

II

"AT HOME, BELOVED, AT HOME"

EVIDENCE is lacking that Tricotrin's devotion for the young woman whom he encountered in such grievous circumstances was of a lasting nature. Having related how she preserved him from his dread resolve, one would rejoice to add that thereafter she exercised upon his career an exalting and abiding influence, but all ascertainable facts seem to indicate that the attachment was brief. It is said, indeed, that on the morrow she referred to the dread resolve in terms of derision. Be this as it may, the girl appears to have transferred her interest to another suitor at a date which points painfully to lightness of conduct. Moreover, there is reason to fear that Tricotrin's laments at her desertion must be ascribed to poetic licence. Nothing in the following records, gathered impartially from the next three or four years of a youth which alas! can only be described as ill-spent, leads us to infer that Delphine remained the dominant factor in the poet's life.

Tricotrin was residing at Montmartre. It was in this quarter of Paris that he had established himself when he spurned the path of commerce in Lyons to write the blank verse tragedies which have not been performed yet; it was here that he displayed later such base ingratitude towards the excellent uncle who had offered him a future in silk that the worthy mohsieur Rigaud had elaborately cursed him. Though it has been affirmed by Anglo-Saxon commentators more than once that he was a denizen of the Quartier Latin, the statement may be dismissed as erroneous; the poet's choice was ever Montmartre. Financial considerations impelled him to manifold changes of domicile, but he was constant to the locality.

As usual, he was residing in a garret. The room contained two beds, of which the second was occupied by his best friend, Nicolas Pitou, the Futurist composer. Little Pitou was responsible for half the rent. The comrades' social circle, which was both artistic and extensive, consisted chiefly of young men who had also acquired a wide experience of Parisian garrets in a comparatively short space of time.

On a certain wet day in June, when Paris had begun to give up all hope of seeing a self-respecting summer that year, Tricotrin chanced to meet one of these young men—Didier by name, a painter. And the painter remarked to the poet, "Do you know there is something mysterious about our pal the novelist? That silly ass Lajeunie is very queer lately."

"He gets up thinner every morning," replied

Tricotrin. "It is sad, but I should not describe it as 'mysterious.' Experience has proved to me that ambition and high thoughts constitute a meagre diet."

"Well, but listen! he does not buy nourishment when he has the means—that is the strange part. A few days ago he called upon me to confide that he was starving, and I lent him sixteen sous. I do not say it vaingloriously, but I was touched and I lent him sixteen sous."

"It was a handsome action."

"Well, a few minutes afterwards I chanced to see him on the boulevard, and his furtive air prompted me to keep an eye on him. Figure yourself my feelings when he slunk into the establishment where you drop discs into a slot to listen to tunes on the Pathéphone! It costs four sous a melody, that distraction; and, as heaven is my witness, he squandered the whole of my loan before he left the place. Trembling with indignation I stood and watched him through the window."

"Really? That was scandalous of him to borrow your sixteen sous and squander it on tunes. Now you come to mention it, I have seen him hanging about that establishment more than once lately. I was never aware that music was one of his weaknesses?"

"Nor I," returned the painter. "I hope he is not going out of his mind."

"I shall look into the matter," said Tricotrin. "I take an interest in Lajeunie."

And having made inquiries in the interval, he said to Pitou that evening:

"Nicolas, has it ever been your view that Lajeunie was uncommonly musical?"

"Lajeunie?" echoed Pitou. "The poor lad has no more taste for music than a Pom."

"Well, it will astonish you to learn that it has become a secret vice with him. I am told in the quartier that he has been borrowing money right and left, and there is every reason to suppose that he lavishes it all upon tunes on the Pathéphone. Moreover, to judge by his emaciated appearance, his professional income is all chucked in the same weird way. It appears to have become a mania with the poor fellow."

"One must have a talk with him!" said Pitou, shocked. "Music is the divinest of the arts, but I do not approve of the form his devotion takes."

"Let us put on our hats and step round to his place without delay," suggested Tricotrin. "I am of your own opinion—it is a crisis that calls for the intervention of his friends."

Lajeunie was at this period lodging on a fifth floor in an unsavoury court that was named the "City of Repose"; and when the artists had climbed to his attic the literary man was discovered in reverie, with his heels upon a manuscript on the table. His face brightened at their entrance.

"I trust that we are not interrupting the flow of composition?" said the twain simultaneously.

"On the contrary, I am rejoiced to see you," declared the author. "It must be Providence that guided you here. Not to beat about the bush, every editor that I have called on to-day has been 'engaged,' and my purse is as void as my interior. You find me ravenous. Positively I am sinking with exhaustion. Could either of you oblige me with a small sum to get a meal?"

The visitors exchanged glances.

"Alas! our accounts at the Banque de France and the Crédit Lyonnais are both overdrawn," said Pitou. "It is a most unfortunate coincidence. I tell you what, however: you can come back with us and share our dinner, which for once in a way is ample."

The hopeful expression on the features of the novelist faded. "If you could make it four sous instead, dear old boy," he said desperately, "it would suit me better."

"Lajeunie," said Tricotrin in solemn tones, "you are not being open with us. Our offer does not touch the spot. Now why? To the ravenous, a share of an ample dinner is worth more than four sous. Avow the truth and say that you seek the coppers to gratify some ignoble passion!"

"Not at all," stammered Lajeunie; "my condition speaks for itself—I am reduced to skin and bone. Look at my arm!" And he took off his coat and displayed a very skinny arm indeed.

"We are not discussing your weight," said Pitou; "let us keep to the point. Besides, you were always as thin as they make them."

"Lajeunie," urged the poet, "we are your friends, and we realise that to err is human; we will be gentle with you; we will help you to conquer the craving. But make a clean breast of it! Come, come; is it not a fact that, were we to supply you with the funds you seek, you would forthwith slip a disc into a slot and dissipate them on a phonograph?"

Lajeunie started. "Since all is known, I shall not stoop to make denials," he groaned, pulling down his shirt sleeve.

"You admit it, then?" said Pitou: "All those loans that you have been raising in the quartier, on the plea of an empty stomach, have gone down slots? You have imposed on good hearts to gratify this corroding vice?"

"I have imposed on no good heart," objected Lajeunie with hauteur. "In saying that I had an empty stomach, my statements have been strictly accurate. If I nevertheless preferred to apply the money to the Pathéphone, that was my affair. What right has anybody to complain of that? I have not shrunk from applying my own money to it."

"Lajeunie," persisted the poet, "we seek your confidence. Our expostulations are dictated by an affectionate interest in your case. Is it not so, Nicolas?"

"It is!" affirmed Pitou. "We will not bully-rag you, old chap; if I spoke harshly, I ask your pardon. You may confide in us without misgiving —we shall be as mild as ducklings, I assure you."

"As ducklings!" repeated Tricotrin. "You will realise that, to the cursory view, the craving of an ill-nourished literary man to drop all his cash down slots appears surprising? Will you not explain to us the fascination of the course? Let us analyse it together. Let us make an effort to extricate you from the snare of this damnable invention! What is the ulterior motive—is it that you aspire to have heard all the records in the répertoire before you die? Believe me, the ambition is hopeless; you will have gone to your last account before you have exhausted even the list of orchestral selections."

"I do not listen to the orchestral selections," demurred Lajeunie sulkily; "I listen to the song, *At Home, Beloved, At Home.*"

"But not always *At Home, Beloved, At Home?*"

"Yes, always. When I have the means I listen to it twice. The other day a friend lent me sixteen sous, and I set the indicator at the song four times running."

The young men regarded him with consternation.

"You have not noticed any other distressing symptoms, Lajeunie?" inquired Tricotrin very gently. "No pains in the head, or lapses of memory?"

"No, I have noticed nothing of the sort, thank you. I am as right in my head as you—and a damned sight righter."

"But, mon ami," remonstrated the musician, "the song is commonplace in the extreme. If you want to set indicators at songs four times running, wait till my opera is produced. In the duet I have just written between the Tenor and Soprano you will hear a descending scale of great thirds that terminates in a wild orgie of consecutive fifths. It is superb. The voices sing the major E and C; the wood wind play a full chord of B major; the harps play chromatic scales *ad lib,* and the brass thunder out the love motif in B flat. *At Home, Beloved, At Home* is muck."

"You do not understand," faltered Lajeunie, beginning to cry; "it is not the technical excellence of the song that allures me—it is Her Voice! I adore her, and we are apart. I cannot endure it. The only respite to my despair is to hear her sing on the phonograph."

"Sapristi! it is love!" ejaculated Pitou.

And with a gesture of supreme relief Tricotrin panted: "Oh, my dear boy, what a burden you have lifted from my mind! I was becoming very anxious about you. You love, and you listen to her on the phonograph? That is rational, that is entirely sane; all my misgivings are removed. Who is she?"

"She is called Amélie Constant. A blonde.

Ravishing. She has a smile that thrills. . . . It is a long story."

"No matter," said Pitou, "no matter; let us have it, I beg!"

"It began some months ago. I could not pay my rent in the rue Legendre, and they turned me out late at night. It was freezing. There was no prospect of a bed. I decided to order a bock in a cheap night café and take shelter there till the morning."

"Not a bad scheme!"

"It grew tedious by five o'clock. And the waiter kept looking at my glass, to see if it was empty yet; I would never have believed that a drink could be made to last so long. There was a girl who sang *At Home, Beloved, At Home*. Veritably an artist! She wore a black lace frock. I marvelled at her being there. Quite young, too. It was only my interest in her that kept me from nodding off. I wished to make her acquaintance, but I did not dare to expect it, because the beer had left me stoney; one cannot very well open a conversation with a lady when it is impossible to say, 'May I offer you some refreshment, mademoiselle?'"

"Don't elaborate the obvious!"

"Well, the crowd kept thinning—the café became drearier every quarter of an hour. At last there was scarcely anybody left but two tinselled dancing girls, gaping in a corner, and the right girl, and myself. I spoke to her then and chanced it. I said, 'It is not exactly rollicking?'

" 'It is enough to give one the hump,' she said; 'why on earth don't you go away?'

"I said, 'I have nowhere to go. Why don't *you?*—have you got to sing any more?'

" 'No,' she said. 'But I always sit here like this till it is broad daylight.'

" 'You always sit here till it is broad daylight? What, even if you are left here by yourself?'

" 'Yes,' she said; 'I have a lonely walk; and the apaches watch these places for us girls to leave —I am afraid of being murdered if I go before it's light.'

"Figure yourself the girl, half dead with sleep, waiting regularly for the day to break, lest she should be murdered on her way home! Is it not literary?"

"Admirable," assented the poet with gusto. "It appeals to me very much indeed."

"I intend to make use of it, myself," said Lajeunie warningly.

"Well, why did she not lodge somewhere else, instead?" asked Pitou.

"That was a point that I put to her. I learnt that she was a stranger in Paris. Also that she did not propose to remain at the café for a day longer than was necessary. Next, as she was so tired, I volunteered to protect her on the walk if she liked to go at once. But I am not of Herculean build, and she said she would rather wait. So we

went on talking. I repeat that I was stoney broke
—and she conversed with me till seven o'clock in
the morning! It is not every girl who would have
done so much as that."

"Oh, it is evident that she has qualities!" said
Tricotrin.

"The sun had risen when we climbed together
to the Butte. Already I recognised a kindred
soul. I parted from her at her door with the understanding that I would see her at the café again
as soon as I contrived to raise the wherewithal
for another bock; her gaze dwelt deeply on me
as she said how earnestly she hoped that I should
not have the key of the street that night too. Well,
her good wishes appeared to bring me fortune—
by midday I had made a sale! An editor to whom
I had offered a hundred-thousand-word serial six
months before proved willing to pay a hundred
and twenty francs for it; and after a strenuous
tussle I extracted a louis from him on account.
Before I broke my fast I sent a telegram, inviting
her to supper."

"It was well done," said the composer, "very
diligent!"

"How sweet were her felicitations when we
met! How divine were now the days that saw
the flowering of a mutual love! I implored her
to seek an engagement worthier of her talents
without loss of time. I indicated a theatrical
agent to her. In our first interview with this
worthy he was sanguine of serving her very speed-

ily; but after we had parted with the fee that he exacted for entering her name in his books, his confidence diminished. I racked my brains for other methods to advance her. It was thanks to my indomitable energies and a stroke of luck that she touched a bit for the phonograph record. A little later she secured an offer for the Chorus in the theatre round the corner; it was to reopen during the last week of May with a revival of *La Fille de Madame Angot*. Would to heaven that she had gone there!"

"Why did she not go there?"

"She did not go there because, no sooner had she settled to do so, than up popped a prospect somewhere else! There was a person who had arranged to open an *al-fresco* theatre on June 1 in the park at Ville-Nogent. He was enthusiastic about her voice, absolutely enthusiastic! He urged her to give the other show the go-by. He pointed out that, with him, she would have better parts and more satisfactory terms. How could we hesitate? To be sure, it was a suburb and I should have tram fares to pay when I went to see her, but it's an imperfect world. She asked the people round the corner to cancel her engagement, and they resentfully did so. This was the commencement of my misery."

"Proceed!"

"We had reckoned without the temperature! Towards the end of May the fellow told her that unless the weather speedily grew milder he should

not open before the 8th. And towards the 8th he
said that, the evenings being still so chilly, it
would be madness to open before the 15th. And
when the 15th approached he explained that the
tardy summer rendered an open-air season so
highly speculative that he was compelled to reduce his programme and dispense with her services altogether. You may be sure I went to see
him. I said:

"'Mon Dieu! Mademoiselle Constant has can-
celled an agreement elsewhere at your earnest
solicitation!'

"He said, 'I regret infinitely, but I have no
more to say about it.'

"I said, 'That cat won't jump. You engaged
the lady, and we hold you to your contract.'

"He said, 'Well, when you produce the contract
we will talk again!'

"Of course, there was *no* written contract. The
man was a black-hearted villain, but we had to
give him best. Her situation was desperate now
—my resources were at their last gasp, and soon
she was on the verge of destitution. Nothing was
possible but for her to return to her stepmother
at Lizy-sur-Ourcq! There are emotions too terrible for words to paint. We sobbed on each
other's necks. We sobbed for hours. Ah, that
parting! When she had gone, the animation of
the streets was torture to me; I staggered to the
Cemetery and flung myself, face downward, upon
the turf. The other mourners respected my be-

reavement—they passed me with hushed tones. Since then my days and nights have been unspeakable. Life yields but one suspension of the agony—to hear her sing upon the phonograph the song she used to sing upon my heart. *At Home, Beloved, At Home!* It shows me each fleeting expression on her mobile face; once more I regain the humble room that was transfigured by our tenderness. *At Home, Beloved, At Home!* I feel the flutter of her breath upon my cheek, the clasp of the loving arms that made home Heaven. And then—crackle-popple-bump! The apparatus stops short, the dream is over—and naught is left me in my desolation but the frenzied hope of borrowing four sous again."

"Lajeunie," quavered Tricotrin, dashing away tears, "we have done you a grave injustice. I am rejoiced that we have had this talk—it will enable me to re-establish you in the esteem of the quartier."

"Mon pauvre ami!" wept Pitou. "We have wronged you bitterly. Something shall be done, Lajeunie! In the circumstances that scoundrel must be forced to engage her. Is it not so, Gustave?"

"Obviously," said Tricotrin. "Courage, cocky, we will arrange matters for you yet! Your pals may not be wealthy, but they are multitudinous; do not figure yourself that you will be allowed to pine into a grave for lack of influence. Your need is urgent, and we shall hold a council on your affair forthwith. See you to-morrow. Again, be brave!" And putting him upon his honour to expend the whole amount on viands, the pair lent him forty sous, and, after embracing him tenderly, departed to enlighten Didier.

Within a couple of hours many artistic heads had been put together. And since it was not the custom of that circle to allow grass to grow beneath their feet in such emergencies as appealed to them, they passed a resolution that delegates should wait upon the recreant manager the following day.

At this stage of the proceedings it was discovered that the poet and Pitou had omitted to ascertain his name and address. The question arose whether he was to be found at Ville-Nogent; perhaps the unpropitious skies had delayed his opening again?

"Gentlemen," said Tricotrin, "I move that the meeting be adjourned for twenty minutes, while we run back to inquire."

"The poor devil will be bucked to hear of the progress we have made," he remarked to Pitou, as they sped along. And as they passed a brilliantly lighted window, through which absorbed figures were visible with their elbows on the tables and receivers clapped to their ears, "There is the fatal place!" he added. "Fortunately——" The words that he was about to speak remained unuttered, and Pitou clutched him by the arm. At that instant one of the heads inside had been raised, and with a throb of horror they saw that the victim had succumbed once more.

"Mon Dieu!" shuddered Tricotrin: "this is frightful."

The novelist came blindly out—in his eyes the dazed stare of a slave to some insidious drug. As they confronted him, he trembled violently, and stood speechless.

"Apostate!" thundered Tricotrin. "Are you lost to all self-control?"

"Pardon!" moaned Lajeunie, "pardon!"

"It exceeds the limits of forbearance," stormed Pitou. "We trusted you; we put faith in your vows of reformation!"

"You were right," sobbed the culprit. "I meant all I said. No one has ever meant anything more nobly."

"In less than two hours you are at it again! Have you eaten? We insist upon the truth—how many goes have you paid for in there?"

"Mercy!" wailed Lajeunie. "It is a passion stronger than myself. I didn't want to do it."

"Do not quote miserable songs to us! How many? Reply!"

"Ten," whimpered the author.

"Morbleu! Has this sinister machine entirely undermined your reason? Are you bent on suicide? Has it robbed you of the last remnants of prudence and common sense?"

"C'est plus fort que moi!" repeated Lajeunie. "Have you no hearts? Can you not realise the witchery? Do not scold me, for I am grateful to you with all my being. If you divined the quarter-of-an-hour's rapture that you have given to me! Space was annihilated. Her voice caressed me as of yore; I saw her smile; I bowed my head upon her breast——''

"You told us all that in your room," interrupted the poet. "I do not say that I cannot comprehend the drunken fascination, but forty sous is a lot of money. If you had taken even five turns I might find excuses for you. But ten! It is an orgy for a millionaire."

"Deliberately I did not mean to take ten—I was tempted one by one. Each time the awakening crackle-popple-bump came, I said, 'Just one dream more!' Be pitiful! It asks for superhuman strength to live sundered from the woman you love when you know that you have only to lift two tubes off hooks to hear her."

"Of course there is something in what you say," conceded the composer; "nobody denies it. Well, look here, your affair is going swimmingly! Everybody is deeply interested. We are assembled at the Bel Avenir—you will go there with us. And as you are totally irresponsible, we shall see that you are fed there! Step lively, now!"

The Council was apprised that the manager was a monsieur Cupillat. Whether the Théâtre Sous Bois had inaugurated its season at Ville-Nogent Lajeunie could not say, but the dastard was believed to be staying at a pension-de-famille in the suburb.

On the morrow, therefore, Tricotrin, accompanied by Sanquereau, the sculptor, who was chosen because he had a frock-coat, and could simulate a dry, attorney-like tone, proceeded by an electric tram to interview the gentleman. Tricotrin, who had no frock-coat, carried a black portfolio, such as those in which grave advocates may be seen transporting legal documents. The sight of the portfolio had encouraged Lajeunie considerably; he felt that it could scarcely fail to impress monsieur Cupillat with the danger of his ways.

"It will not do to lose one's temper with him," observed Sanquereau, as the tram bounded and crashed over the course in its native manner; "we shall have more effect if we are ominously calm."

"Understood!" panted the poet, struggling to retain his seat. "But I wish these untamed trams did not always make me feel sick."

Their ring at the bell of the pension-de-famille evoked a crimson-faced woman of vast dimensions. Beholding two strangers, whom she took for prospective boarders, she beamed upon them with a solicitude that was well-nigh maternal, but on learning that they merely wished to see monsieur Cupillat, she snapped that he was "at the show," and promptly returned to the kitchen.

The park was easily discoverable, however, and some minutes later they found themselves in the presence of the entrepreneur himself. Perhaps by reason of the thermometer, which remained depressing to one who was committed to open an *al-fresco* theatre in three days' time, his brow was dark.

"Eh bien, messieurs? What is it? I have my hands full."

"Monsieur," began the sculptor judicially, "our affair concerns the engagement that you entered into with mademoiselle Amélie Constant. It appears that you hesitate to fulfil your undertaking."

"I do not hesitate—I know nothing about it."

"Permettez! Influenced by your representations, mademoiselle Constant, hereinafter referred to as 'The Artist,' renounced a lucrative arrangement in another quarter."

"Listen, monsieur!" broke in the faithless Cupillat sharply. "I have no leisure to attend to these rigmaroles. My business presses!"

"Permettez! The maintenance of amicable relations between the Manager and The Artist is a matter so much to be desired that we should be loth to think that in our client's interests we shall be compelled to resort to extremities. The case may still be settled out of Court. This offer is made without prejudice."

"And it is our earnest hope," added Tricotrin, "that after our little conference has concluded you will be induced to take a broader and more enlightened view of a question so important to the local development of dramatic enterprise.''

"A word in your ear!" said Cupillat. "Also without prejudice. You may go to the devil!"

"It is like that, you blackleg, is it?" stuttered Sanquereau in a fury. "I have a good mind to kick you in the eye."

"Let us dip him in the canal!" suggested Tricotrin, white with rage.

"A couple of trumpery students!" muttered Cupillat, backing hurriedly. "I snap my fingers at you and your 'client'!"

"Students!" spluttered the emissaries, frantic at the insult. "We are no students, you ignorant ape—we are full-blown. And you will see if you can snap your fingers at us! Since courtesy is unappreciated, we will try other measures, voyons! We have not done with you."

"Get out!" scoffed Cupillat, who was already at some distance from them.

"It is war!" bellowed the pair. And after the parties had gesticulated a good deal, Cupillat dived into his little wooden theatre, and slammed the door with derision.

"By the Powers, it is war!" swore Sanquereau, gritting his teeth.

"It is war to the knife!" asseverated Tricotrin vengefully.

"After this, he shall take her, or I will hound him out of the place!"

"I will burst his infernal show up!" vowed

the poet. And then, as they began to recover
their mental balance, "But—but—I say! Precisely
—er—what is there we can do?"

Sanquereau looked blank:

"We shall have to consider—another Council
must be summoned. One thing is certain, the
question of expense must not be allowed to deter
us! Personally, I would pawn my shoes for a
chance to get even with the ruffian."

And that was the view taken by the Assembly.
In his stirring appeal for a Fund, Didier cried:
"Gentlemen, to-day we have to bear in mind,
more than the rights of an artiste, more than the
sufferings of a comrade. Obloquy has been heaped
on our ambassadors, and nothing less than the
Honour of the Quartier is at stake! Had I jewels,
I would strip them from me in the sacred cause.
I guarantee two francs!"

It illustrates the spirit of the Convocation when
it is stated that as much as twenty-nine francs
forty-five centimes was subscribed even before
anybody had the least idea how the Fund would
advance matters. One member, less public-spirited
than the rest, had asked for information on this
point at the termination of the speech. He said,
"Impressed as I am by the fervour of the last
speaker, I rise to inquire what the desired Fund
is for?" Didier, with a sublime gesture, had replied in a single word, "Conquest!" And the
cheers were deafening. Pitou's feeble tenor
started *La Marseillaise*.

It was after *La Marseillaise* had been chorused that a plan of campaign was sought.

"It is now," said the President, "that we must determine how to apply this noble expression of widespread sympathy. Splendid as our finances are, they will not suffice for us to open an opposition show and bring the blackguard to his knees in that way. Has any chap a suggestion to offer?"

An ominous silence fell. Seconds ticked past, each more fateful than its predecessor. Boys turned to one another with haggard eyes.

At this crisis, a reputation was brilliantly enhanced. Beginning in a firm yet modest voice, "Monsieur le President, and other rotters, I would direct attention to the fact that a powerful ally is the weather," a member proceeded to outline a proposal which first puzzled, then captivated, and finally swept the House to enthusiasm. He resumed his seat amid salvoes of applause. The member was M. Gustave Tricotrin, the poet.

Truth to tell, it was more like March than midsummer, the evening on which the lamps of the Théâtre Sous Bois at Ville-Nogent were lit at last. Nevertheless, the spot being as dismal as any other suburb of Paris, a sparse audience had risked colds in the head to seek distraction. They wore stout boots because the ground was damp. The depressed Cupillat, in the pay-box between two gloomy poplars, was not kept too busy to observe that a score of strangers filtered into the cheaper seats—young men who in no wise re-

sembled the respectable bourgeoisie of Ville-Nogent; he inferred that there must be an art school
somewhere in the vicinity, and was encouraged
by the prospect of its continued patronage.

The programme announced:

"SPECTACLE VARIÉ EN TOUS GENRES
COMÉDIE, VAUDEVILLE,
ROMANCE
CHANSONNETTES, DUOS, RÉCITS
DANSES,
SCÈNES COMIQUES."

The little curtain rose jerkily, and a lady of
mature age advanced towards the six footlights
to recite.

In the middle of the final stanza, one of the
strange young men in the front row sneezed with
such alarming violence that heads turned to him.
The lady looked disconcerted, and several persons in his neighbourhood, who had hitherto appeared fairly cheerful, shivered from sympathy.

The lady concluded. And the young man got up,
and stamping hard, commenced to promote circu-
lation by a swift arm-and-leg exercise. Some
minutes later an equally tremendous sneeze ex-
ploded from a young man in the centre benches.
Two matrons, sitting behind him, exchanged an
apprehensive glance, and a solicitous parent
folded a pocket-handkerchief around his offspring's neck. "One must, my little one; it makes
cold, voyons!" he said in urgent tones.

At the expiration of half an hour the number of artistic young men who were shuddering turbulently was so extensive, and the reports of brobdingnagian sneezes were so continuous, that all the spectators had hunched their shoulders in misgiving. During the sprightly vaudeville a racking cough from Sanquereau was succeeded by a paroxysm from Pitou; and before the duos were reached Lajeunie was stumbling, with chattering teeth, over a dozen pairs of feet in his haste to flee from further danger.

His prudence was emulated, at brief intervals, by nineteen other young men, obviously chilled to the bone. The solicitous parent decided that it was no place for his offspring, and the child was dragged forth, protesting loudly. Fear had now spread like an epidemic, and vacant seats displayed themselves every minute.

The next evening the audience was more exiguous still. But it contained twenty young men who again demonstrated to the public the severity of the maladies that they were likely to contract by patronising this entertainment.

When the exodus began, MM. Tricotrin and Sanquereau found their way barred by a raging manager:

"You bandits!" foamed Cupillat, "beware of the police. Do not figure yourselves you will do this devil's work to-morrow—I shall recognise the faces of you all and you will be refused admission!"

"My poor fellow," replied Tricotrin, "we are as manifold as the sands of Sahara. We could provide a fresh contingent every night for a year —and we shall have settled your hash in a week! The police? It is not criminal to sneeze. However, if you should feel inclined to strengthen your attractions by a certain engagement, I do not say but what we might find the temperature more genial."

On the following Monday the bills of the Théâtre Sous Bois proclaimed the appearance of a Mlle. Amélie Constant. She sang *At Home, Beloved, At Home,* and nineteen young men, to say nothing of the ecstatic Lajeunie, were so enchanted by her gifts that her performance made a veritable furore.

III

Monsieur Blotto and the Lions

SOON after Pitou had stooped to accept an engagement as pianist at a Bioscope on the Butte, pending acclamation of his operas, he was dismissed for incompetence. He went home thoughtfully. It was the day that Tricotrin's mystical play, *The Goblin Child's Mother,* had met with its seventeenth rejection, and the composer had left him in their attic debating suicide.

"We shall divide the biggest hump in Paris to-night, Tricotrin and I!" reflected poor Pitou, toiling to the sixth floor.

Judge of his astonishment to find his tidings received with a shrug! "It is of scant importance that you have got the sack," said the dramatic poet negligently. "In truth, as the job was an insult to your genius, I was at the point of counselling you to resign it. Between us two is it not, always, one heart and one purse?"

"Hein?" faltered Pitou. "But—pardon the supposition—if the purse is empty? Have our calamities turned your brain? How about the suicide you were projecting?"

"Suicide? What suicide?" said the other young man, bewildered. "Ah yes, I remember,

54

I did make some allusion to such a Curtain! Well,
all that is past; things have happened since you
went out—I adopt a new career, and what is mine
is yours.''

"The work, or the wage?" inquired Pitou.
"Expound before I sign!"

"You shall share them both. I entered journalism—and when my own mendacity fails, you can
draw upon yours to assist me.''

"It sounds propitious," Pitou acknowledged.
"But the transition from laudanum is a bit ab-
rupt. So far from being defunct, you are buoyant, and I lack a scenario of the intermediate Act.
Am I to conclude that the postman has been?"

"The conclusion would be happy. I have had
a letter from a relative; and I would not have you
judge the whole of my family by the uncle who
was tactless enough to disturb your repose;* the
man Rigaud, after all, is but an uncle by marriage. Some of my relatives have mitigating
qualities. This one has been discoursing upon my
talents to a friend who has indulged his literary
tastes by becoming a newspaper proprietor; he
has acquired *La Dépêche de Montbonne,* and pro-
poses to wake it up. In fine, it is contemplated
that a weekly feature of the organ shall be a column of theatrical intelligence from Paris, contributed by myself.''

"If this comes off," exclaimed Pitou with ela-

---

* The disgraceful incident to which the poet manifestly refers in
these unseemly terms has been recorded in the volume *A Chair on
the Boulevard.*

tion, "we may be able to see the inside of a theatre sometimes."

"I anticipate the novelty. And even if the card of the Montbonne critic should be spurned at the Paris box offices, which is not impossible, that will be no reason why I should fail to read the notices in the *Figaro* and express the same statements in choicer words. As for the desired sprinkling of green-room gossip, nothing could be simpler or more generous than for us to invent an epigram once a week and put it into the pretty mouth of a popular actress whom we do not know. Mon Dieu! this enterprising tyro of Montbonne will get a bargain in me."

"The sordid commercial aspect of the case is represented by what figure?"

"It has still to be determined, but whatever it is, I foresee that I shall be worth more. Always the same story—the simplicity of youth is taken advantage of!"

Time passed, in which much fasting was accomplished. And then there was a memorable morning on which Tricotrin began to refer to himself loftily as "We dramatic critics," and to peruse the notices in the *Figaro* with care. At the start he found his opinions of performances at which he had not been present in agreement with the views of the *Figaro*—one must toddle before one runs—but later he differed from them. His impressions of a play at the Renaissance, which he had not seen, were entirely independent. And

he "chatted" and "supped" with so many prominent persons in his paragraphs that he was often
startled to realise that he wasn't on nodding terms
with them, or in a position to have any supper.

"As you predicted," Pitou remarked, "for a
journalist who keeps such distinguished company,
the salary is slight! Now one comes to think of it,
it does not warrant the cost of the imaginary telephone on which the celebrities ring you up to give
you their confidences."

"Your objection is just," owned Tricotrin.
"But remember that our distant Editor assumes
that I was on the telephone before I was on the
Dépêche. I could not part with my invisible telephone—do not ask me; it is a fountain of perpetual inspiration. Why, to-morrow Yvette Guil-
bert is going to ring me up, the moment she re-
turns from London, to tell me her professional
worries and beg for my advice. As she will be
prostrated by the journey, I am not sure but what,
'yielding to her entreaties, I may even jump into
an auto-taxi and take potluck in her delightful
home.' The only drawback is, that when we dine
on our herrings I shall recall the pleasing fancy
and be resentful of the exiguous facts. I was op-
pressed by discontent of that nature after my
anecdote beginning, 'Five of us were lunching at
the Restaurant de la Cascade.' Never had I felt a
sandwich to do less for me."

But if the contrast between his festivities in
print and his economies in the garret were at

times confusing to the critic, he was sensible of a clear appreciation on the days that cheques arrived. And the autumn flagged, and still the modest payments came. "It looks like something out of a sensational romance," he confessed; "for the first time I find myself able to grasp the meaning of the term 'permanent' in relation to income!" And as Pitou had submitted to another insult to his genius and was on a pay list too, the pair promenaded the boulevard Rochechouart with the air of *rentiers*.

Misgiving arose suddenly. It was communicated that the Editor was at the point of passing a couple of days in the capital and desired an interview; monsieur Tricotrin was requested to call at a certain hotel on the following afternoon at "half-past seventeen."

"Not content with arriving to shatter our peace," complained the Critic, "he must make his appointment according to the New Notation, which I shall never comprehend! I lose trains nowadays while I am doing arithmetic to find out at what hour they go."

"Half-past seventeen is Delirium for half-past five," interpreted Pitou. "And why should his arrival have that dire effect?"

"I cannot explain. Though I am, of course, aware that the virtues of my 'copy' are incontestable, something whispers that the man's appearance on the scene is not in our highest interests. It is not that I contemplate his disturbing our privacy and noting the non-existent telephone and the absence of furniture; neither is it that I distrust the adequacy of my best trousers if I expend two sous on turpentine; but I would that he had remained in Montbonne! It is a mysterious instinct.''

''My own impression,'' declared the composer, ''is that his project is to invigorate you with viands, and dazzle you with a rise. If you get a chance to name the beverage say 'volnay'—I am told that one feels it for a long time.''

''Well, your surmise may be correct,'' admitted Tricotrin; ''I suppose, if I were not a pessimist by nature, I should not doubt it.''

And having bought the turpentine and hung the trousers outside the window all the next morning, he polished his boots ruminantly, and went forth to the hotel.

The mysterious instinct to which he had referred was strong as he inquired at the bureau if monsieur Blotto was within, and when he had ascended to the salon he was not stimulated by the aspect of a self-important gentleman with a fussy manner.

''Monsieur Tricotrin,'' said the gentleman, ''happy to see you!''

''An ass with a swelled head!'' determined Tricotrin. And he responded: ''Too amiable, monsieur. Enchanted. It is a joy to which I have long looked forward.''

''Sit down, sit down,'' said his employer. ''I

am happy that you are punctual—I have an engagement shortly, and I desired a chat with you before going out.''

"No repast, morbleu!'' was the Critic's thought. "Now I wonder if a plea for credit is on the road?''

But a very few seconds sufficed to dispel that fear.

"Your 'copy,' '' observed monsieur Blotto, "affords me great satisfaction—great satisfaction. I am not without a hope that a day may come when we shall be in a position to make the payment—er—more commensurate with the merits of your work.''

" 'A day may come' is a rotten kind of date,'' mused Tricotrin, bowing his acknowledgments— "so much for Pitou as a prophet!'' Aloud he repeated: "Too amiable, monsieur! I avow that in accepting a nominal emolument I was strongly actuated by the conviction that you would spring a bit very soon.''

" 'Very soon' is too much to say,'' answered the other; "for some little time I am afraid we must leave matters as they are.''

Tricotrin, infinitely relieved, strove to attain the expression of one who had received a shock. And monsieur Blotto continued: "I shall not disguise from you that the tone of your column is a shade too Parisian for the majority of our readers at present. We must educate them by degrees— by degrees! Hitherto the Montbonne Press has

failed woefully in its duty—it has not been alive to its responsibilities—for that reason I was tempted to acquire the paper. Under the new régime it will be a force—I write many of the leaders myself. I do not profess to be conversant with all the technical details of editorship, but what I bring to *La Dépêche* is a Directing Brain. I bring initiative, culture, taste."

"The pre-eminent gifts!" affirmed Tricotrin. "Many of the leaders, if I may dare to hint it, have electrified me by their vigour." And mentally he inquired, "Was it to tell me how talented he is that he has dragged me down from Montmartre?"

Monsieur Blotto beamed. He offered him a cigarette. "Personally I take much interest in your little intimate anecdotes of the artistic strata," he resumed; "to a man like myself they are, I need scarcely tell you, most congenial. You are younger than I had pictured you, monsieur."

"Ah!" said the Critic portentously, "my few summers have provided vast experience."

"And Paris is a swift professor, hein?"

'For those in the right class there are indeed opportunities to learn!"

"And how, for example, did you secure promotion to that class at your early age?"

It began to reveal itself to Tricotrin that under his amateur Editor's efforts to impress him was something akin to envy. "Mon Dieu!" he drawled, "one must remember that I am, before all else, dramatic poet. Do not figure yourself that, because an author's plays are not yet staged, he is necessarily unknown to the managers and artists of the Boulevard; an agreement for a drama is made long before the drama is produced, and in the inner circles its qualities remain no secret. I do not hesitate to say that a man may achieve a reputation the most conspicuous among those whose judgment is authoritative some years before the public have even heard his name.''

"It is strangely fascinating, the artistic life!" exclaimed the provincial, who was now all attention. And then, not wishing to appear ignorant, he made haste to add, "Of course, I was aware that such conditions prevailed, but not quite to that extent.''

"It is anomalous, is it not?" said Tricotrin confidentially. "As you see for yourself, I am not above turning out a column of good stuff every week for the merest trifle, and yet—if I do not have an air of boasting—there are at home, in my desk, theatrical contracts for which some of the most highly paid journalists in Paris would give their ears.''

The impromptu fiction was delivered with such engaging candour that it might have imposed upon a more sophisticated listener than monsieur Blotto of Montbonne. It was at this point that his motive for seeking the interview was manifested. Clearing his throat, and disguising eagerness very poorly, he remarked: "Now that I come to think

of it, since I am so rarely in Paris, I might do
worse than take the present opportunity to—to
avail myself of your introductions to a few of the
literary and dramatic stars! It might be agreeable to me to exchange ideas with them."

For some dizzied moments the unfortunate
Critic realised all the sensations of a passenger on
a raging sea. The room rocked about him, and it
was only by one of those efforts which the ro-
mancers call "superhuman" that he contrived to
answer. "I should rejoice!" he faltered. "Now
I wonder if I can postpone an appointment that
I have for this evening? It is of vital consequence,
or naturally I would make no bones about breaking it."

"This evening," rejoined monsieur Blotto, with
appalling promptitude, "I shall not be free either.
So we will say to-morrow!"

"Oh, of course," assented Tricotrin, panic-
stricken, "to-morrow I shall be delighted! Would
you care to call on Sarah Bernhardt—it is not her
'day,' but she is always at home in the afternoon
to intimate friends, and we need not stand on
ceremony."

"It would not be bad," said the Editor, whose
mouth watered at the notion, "but I am not here
on pleasure, and my affairs will keep me busy in
the afternoon. It is not till evening that I shall
be unoccupied."

"In the evening she will be playing," deplored
Tricotrin; "it would not be good enough for us to

run round to her dressing-room—she is always so restless there. We had better make it another day, then!"

"Impossible! To-morrow night I must return to Montbonne. No; what I would propose is that you should take a little dinner with me to-morrow, not too late, at some restaurant in the neighbourhood, and that we should go to some of these people afterwards. It might, for example, be amusing to meet Brieux."

"Peste! I saw him off to the country yesterday; he is full of a new scenario that he was telling me about. Let me think! Is it worth your while to know Lemaître, or Pierre Loti—you would find them both charming fellows?"

"I shall leave the programme to you!" said monsieur Blotto serenely. "Decide as you think best—be with me at a quarter to nineteen sharp!" And having pencilled the figures on his cuff for a mind less tortured to elucidate, the young man made his escape from the hotel, questioning what miracle could occur to save him.

Never had Paris looked to him a harder nut to crack than as he tottered up the hill to his humble abode. Pitou was preparing one of the nocturnal herrings, and turned, paling at his air.

"Cook both," said Tricotrin tersely; "ere long we may lack three sous to buy a couple!"

"A—ah?" shuddered Pitou. "That sacré Editor—there was *no* volnay? What is our latest catastrophe? Would you vote for conference, or nourishment first?"

His jaw dropped as the details were unfolded. The poet and the musician stared at each other with gloomy eyes. For some seconds there was to be heard no sound upon that altar to the Muses save the neglected frizzling of the fish.

"My poor friend," murmured Pitou at last, "I see nothing before you but to be knocked down by an automobile—I shall announce your injuries. To avert the danger of a visit of condolence here, you will have been borne to the nearest hospital, and I shall not specify which one it was."

Tricotrin shook his locks. "I fear," he groaned, "that he might smell a rat—it is pungent. Mon Dieu!" He strode to the broken window and apostrophised the distant chimneys. "O Lutetia, aureate with celebrities—and I cry vainly for but two or three!"

"Well, it would be premature of us to give way to blank verse," said Pitou, "for we have twenty-four hours to turn round in!" He yielded his attention to the herrings. "I shall consider the subject while I am thumping the piano to-night—many of my sublimest inspirations have coruscated while I thumped—and in the meanwhile a felicitous lie may present itself to you also. Upon my word, we were ignoring those two important factors in the case! Taking them into the balance-sheet, I am not disinclined to pronounce the outlook highly hopeful."

"It is true," agreed Tricotrin. "Yes, I declare we had lost sight of our opportunities for reflection—how strange it is that one may overlook the things nearest at hand! Furthermore, when you come back, we will call a council of all the striving spirits of the quartier—if Lajeunie would consent to shave his head, I might pretend he was Rostand."

But when the circumstances were laid before Lajeunie, in the small hours, and a café, the hirsute young novelist firmly refused to shave his head, even to accentuate his resemblance to the author of *Chantecler*. "It is unheard of!" he objected. "I would make many noble sacrifices for you, but baldness goes beyond the limits; as you are well aware, it is with reluctance that I have my hair so much as trimmed. I tell you what, however—I will make you known to my friend, Papa Tripier."

"What are friends of yours worth to me, peacock?" demanded Tricotrin; "I seek superb reputations, not vagrants of your own type."

"How often must I mention that I am welcome in spheres immeasurably above your vacant head?" complained Lajeunie. "Because you are on my visiting-list do you figure yourself that I never make an acquaintance I am not ashamed of? Papa Tripier has a very fine position—he resides in a boarding-house and has three meals every day. Moreover, he is an octogenarian."

"Well, but what is his specialty—what does he

perform on?" Pitou inquired. "Antiquity by itself would not suffice to meet the Editor's requirements."

"You can consider your Papa Tripier 'declined
with thanks,'" said Tricotrin; "the Editor re-
grets that your contribution is below his standard."

"You are wrong," protested Lajeunie. "I
guarantee that he would find it worthy of his
Christmas Number. Papa Tripier has a gift of
the gab that I have rarely known equalled. He
has also a lively affection for the epoch of his late
Majesty Louis-Philippe, 'when everybody possessed an elegance, a wit, a charm totally lost to
the French of to-day, who are nothing but a pack
of voyous! Mais, mon Dieu! que voulez-vous?'
In the prodigious period of the late lamented
Louis-Philippe, a chap could buy a bottle of good
wine for four sous, old sport!"

"Hein? I have always bewailed that I was in
advance of my generation—it appears that I was
born too late!"

"Papa will recount how he heard a great burst
of laughter on the boulevard de Gand—what you
children call the 'boulevard des Italiens'—and
how it was the glorious Dumas himself, the cre-
ator of the *Musketeers,* rollicking round the corner, arm-in-arm with Balzac. And he will tell you
of another burst of laughter from an arbour on a
lawn, and how it was Paul de Kock roaring over
the story he was writing. And he will be eloquent

about de Musset, who was of a 'beauty incomparable,' the cynosure even of the boulevard de Gand—where 'beauty and genius were as abundant, under Louis-Philippe, sapristi! as taxes, and insolence under the sacrée République!' But again, 'Mon Dieu! que voulez-vous?' "

"If this person has any existence outside a novel you are preparing for rejection, which I strongly doubt," said Tricotrin, "I will allow him a small part in the tragedy. As a stop-gap he might have his uses. But I have endeavoured to get it into your skull that it is living, not dead lions I am hunting. Pay for your bock—we shall all proceed to see now if Sanquereau can offer a sane idea!"

Alas! though many intellects were brought to bear upon the problem, not one among them could point the way to living lions. And the night passed, and the sun rose, and the fateful day sped towards a "quarter to nineteen" quicker than any day before.

The Critic's reputation hung upon a hope as slender as a hair, if one may employ a cliché that he himself would have disdained. It was, that the dinner should terminate too late for monsieur Blotto to desire anything except to catch his train; and at least a dozen bohemians volunteered their services to retard the meal.

The Editor was much impressed by his contributor's popularity as the pair bent their steps towards a restaurant—never had he known any-

body to encounter so many acquaintances in so
short a space. And each of them fell upon the
respected scribe with an urgency that brooked no
denial.

"Mon Dieu! you will think me a difficult guest,"
said Tricotrin. "But it is always like this on the
Boulevard when one walks—perhaps we had better take a cab?" And no sooner had he said it
than their way was blocked by Lajeunie!

"Ah, mon cher Tricotrin! What a chance!"
exclaimed Lajeunie. "I was at the point of tele-
graphing to you. We want you to do us the favour to come round to the theatre after the show
—the private office. We are in a dilemma about
Bernstein's play." He burst into a narrative of
the most complicated order, and Tricotrin put in:

"Let me introduce you—monsieur Lajeunie,
monsieur Blotto." Aside to the Editor he explained, "The Literary Adviser to the Gymnase!
I fear we should spare him a moment; would you
much mind our taking a seat somewhere?"

On the terrace of an adjacent café, Lajeunie's
history of the dilemma at the Gymnase, which
scintillated with the most eminent names, was
hardly exhausted when they were hailed by a
sprightly ancient, who proved to be "Papa Tripier" in the flesh. To Tricotrin *sotto voce* the ancient intimated that the hoaxing of editors as a
fine art had flourished solely under Louis-Philippe,
but his public reminiscences of the epoch delayed
the dinner by fully twenty minutes.

"An eccentric!" whispered Tricotrin. "But courted by the most famous personages in Paris. A favourable criticism from his pen is said to make the fortune of any novel written. Ma foi! one meets everybody at this time of day."

And really one seemed to do so, for more alleged notabilities showered about them as he spoke!

"Flamant, the painter—I should have liked you to see his 'Circe' in the Salon!" he mentioned, reflecting that Flamant too would have liked to see it there. "The other man is Sanquereau, the sculptor—many people predict that he will go further than Rodin. The next time you are here you must meet more of the Moderns! This evening, of course, we shall visit people who are fully 'arrived,' but in Paris, you know, we talk more of the men who are making the New Schools than of the old-fashioned lot familiar to the philistine; and as a matter of fact they are more exclusive."

Across his shoulder he had a glimpse of the faithful Pitou, whose duty was to dog their footsteps to the restaurant, and subsequently drift upon them to defer their departure. To-night his piano-thumping would be done by deputy.

Yet the crisis came. Though the composer duly drifted to their presence after the coffee was served, chewing a toothpick; though he was explained to be a Genius, and favoured them with a most fascinating account of a dispute with Messager, monsieur Blotto began to look at his watch. "I had no idea it was so late," he remarked. "If we are to see your friends, monsieur Tricotrin, I am afraid we must be rising. Where do we go first?"

The haggard gaze of the comrades met. The Critic gulped all that was left in his glass. "My project was to run round to Richepin's," he declared, uttering the most illustrious name that presented itself, "but I have not yet heard whether he has anything 'on'—we should have had a message here. I shall at once ring him up! Do not disturb yourself, monsieur Pitou—I pray you remain with monsieur Blotto while the waiter conducts me to the telephone."

How could he foresee that a kindly impulse would move monsieur Blotto to be conducted too?

"Peste!" he panted, his knees failing, "I forget his number."

And next, the friendly Editor was moved to find it for him.

Driven actually to invoke the Exchange for the immortal Richepin, the wretched young man clung to the telephone for support. Upon the brow of Pitou the perspiration broke in beads.

With a celerity unprecedented in France, the number was forthcoming.

"Allô! Allô!" stammered the desperate victim: "monsieur Richepin, is he in? It is monsieur Tricotrin."

And a female voice answered in his ear, "Monsieur Richepin is not at home."

This answer being inaudible to monsieur Blotto and Pitou, the composer's breath was suspended by terror. But all the courage of the Critic was restored. "Ah, I salute you! how are you, dear master?" he cried. "We are praying for your affirmative to my request."

"Monsieur Richepin," the voice repeated, "is not at home."

"Oh, did you? I have not received it yet," continued Tricotrin. "What? Oh, to my rooms, that accounts for it! May we—hein? Yes, he is an Editor of mine, and a most brilliant man."

"What are you saying? Who are you?" squeaked the voice. "I keep telling you monsieur Richepin is out."

"Oh, my honoured friend, I hope it is not violent?" said the Critic for reply. "What? Well, we should be enchanted, but he is leaving Paris this evening."

"Not at home! Not at home! Who is it you are talking to?" yelled the servant, losing patience.

"Most certainly, I shall be overjoyed," returned Tricotrin, "but—— What? Right! the next time he arrives! I will come on Sunday alone, then. Au revoir, cher maître, I so earnestly hope you will pass a good night." And he rang off smartly before the infuriated bonne could anticipate him.

"A touch of his neuralgia!" he announced,

turning. "He is desolated to miss you, but he must go to bed."

Behind Blotto's back the allies gripped hands with relief.

The respite was short, however. Though they resumed their seats, the exigent Blotto was not to be balked of lions. Monsieur Pitou developed an ardent interest in the matter, and he and the Critic debated exhaustively the question of the happiest selection. But the debate could not be continued until the train was imminent.

So, all things being equally impossible, Tricotrin decided that the green-room of the Théâtre Français would amuse his Editor most.

"This," he gasped to Pitou, as the host was putting on his overcoat, "is *your* turn—*I* am played out. Do with him what you will. *But remember that the man must never reach the Français!*"

The night was fair as the trio stepped into the glitter of the boulevard. The Critic, no longer master of himself, leant heavily on the composer's arm. Almost at the same moment he beheld with horror an unpropitious cabman wooing monsieur Blotto to accelerate their doom.

"The Métro," said Pitou peremptorily, "would be quicker!"

At these inspired words Tricotrin nearly bounded with hope. How often had he asserted that one could not cross a road by the Métropolitain without having to change twice!

Monsieur Blotto did not demur.

And the opportunities offered for being on wrong platforms were infinite.

When the tourist was replete with subways and the party climbed disgusted to the street, the loss of time had been extremely serious, and they were farther from the Français than at the start.

"Mon Dieu!" he bemoaned, "there remains to us no more than an hour—no more than an hour; I must call at the hotel for my valise, and my train goes at twenty to zéro."

"It is maddening!" fumed Tricotrin. "What may the time be precisely? Morbleu! If I am not mistaken they are playing what's-its-name to-night—in which case we shall get there when everybody is on the stage; the green-room will be empty for even longer than we can stay. Let us see a journal; perhaps they are playing something else!"

But they were not. It was just as he had feared.

That execrable Métro! For this evening the Français must be scratched.

"Can you suggest no visit hereabouts? Where are we?"

"Montmartre!" sighed Tricotrin; "the Immortal Forty are not so high."

And the Editor's face grew longer still; his dejection grieved his guides.

"Upon my word, gentlemen," said Pitou, "I feel some responsibility for this contretemps, though it may be that I am unduly sensitive. We are, as it happens, in a region not uninteresting.

If monsieur Blotto would peep at what few
strangers are privileged to behold, what says he
to bohemia—the extraordinary quarters where
youths of genius pray to their Muses, and often
to their concierges, and support existence on herrings and hope? I venture the opinion that the
Français would have tickled him less."

"Are you acquainted with any such obscure
young fellows?" asked Tricotrin, startled.

"I know of two," Pitou answered, "not far
distant—a poet and musician."

"It would certainly be droll," agreed the Editor, recovering his cheerfulness.

Up a hill they went, and up six flights of stairs;
and agape, Tricotrin saw Pitou tap at their own
door.

No voice invited them to enter.

"Nevertheless, we may venture in," said Pitou;
"I know them well enough."

Beyond the broken panes the moon was vivid;
stark poverty was revealed before he took the
liberty to light the lamp.

"A poet, and musician," he repeated, "and I
assure you, of talents remarkable! Ah! a herring-
bone, as I predicted; one of them has dined to-
night. What have we here? A scrap of the composer's! 'Rose de Noel,' hein? Refused, I dare
swear, by a score of publishers! Yet one day perhaps the rose will have its vogue. Listen, the
thing is not without merit!" And in his little
tenor voice he sang.

Never had the Critic contemplated his friend with such admiration.

"The table where they write—grimed. The chairs they sit on—broken. The panorama that inspires them—chimney-pots. No, I am wrong— I surmise that they do not note the chimney-pots. Our bohemians look, past the distant roofs, on to the great stage of the Opéra—into the theatres of the Boulevard—into the sumptuous salons of fair women, whose applause they hope to win."

The Editor shone with complacence. Had it been Montbonne, he would have seen only a gaunt garret and the need for soap-and-water—but it was Paris, and he saw the shade of Murger and was charmed. Improved by two artists' visions at the window, the vista of chimney-pots became a memorable view; indeed, he began to feel like two artists himself.

"It is a pity," Pitou continued, "that the poet has not left a verse about."

And, by a stroke of good fortune, an ode of the absent poet's was perceived!—and the Critic had an impulse to declaim it. His sincere appreciation of the manuscript enabled him to do the fullest justice to its beauty.

Monsieur Blotto grew pink with pleasure. Privately he foresaw himself recounting this experience for years to come—in the tone of one to whom Paris held no mysteries. It was with difficulty that he could bear in mind his train at "twenty to zéro."

"I declare we have not fared so badly, after all!" said Tricotrin, as they put him into an auto-taxi at last. "We have chanced to meet many of the Moderns; we have talked with Richepin over the telephone; and we have penetrated to the innermost heart of bohemia."

"I have been vastly interested—vastly interested," concurred the Editor. "Without exaggeration, as pleasant an evening as I have ever spent! If I regret anything, it is merely that the two young fellows were not at home." His acknowledgments were numerous, and only the tooting of the taxi cut them short.

The comrades fell into each other's arms.

"My preserver!" cried the Critic. "Yet I would that he had thanked us less—I confess to compunction."

"The same with me—the Greatest are never wholly content with their achievements," said Pitou. "But we have saved our bacon!" he chirruped, skipping.

"And I am sure," added Tricotrin virtuously, "his nearest, and dearest could not have worked harder than we did to meet his wishes!"

IV

AFTER the foregoing crisis, there is reason to believe, the poet remained on the pay-sheet of *La Dépêche de Montbonne* for several months. Dishonesty often reaps some transient advantage here below, though the youthful reader would be rash to anticipate substantial benefits from its practice unless he is astute. The world is thick with rogues who have never attained to more than the fleeting fiver. But when monsieur Blotto discarded dramatic criticism from Paris in favour of a column of local pleasantries and compliments Tricotrin's position gave him furiously to think. For one thing, he had a nightmare.

"You cannot conceive the horror of it," he moaned to the composer, whom his shrieks had wakened. "A nightmare the most frightful—I dreamt I was thirty. Girls referred to me as a 'fat old thing.' Oh, mon Dieu! light the candle and see if my hair has turned white."

"Thirty must be a wreck of an age," agreed Pitou. "But you will have time to double the contents of the National Library before you are thirty. Be calm!"

"No; it has been sent to me as a warning! I should have been famous and opulent ere this; yet it would be exaggerating to say that I have either world-wide renown or unlimited wealth. Something must be done to give my affairs a leg-up without delay."

"I recommend the Editor of *Le Demi-Mot* to your attention," said Pitou, after thinking the matter over. "If you lay the case before him as cogently as that, he might buy an ode."

"What a head you have! And where should I be without your advice?" cried Tricotrin, his confidence returning. "Yes, you are right; I have been allowing *Le Demi-Mot* far too long a respite —it is more than time that they had the privilege of gathering another flower of my genius. I shall offer them a bouquet of it in the morning."

And after a light luncheon, he selected a round dozen of his rejected manuscripts and went out to conquer.

As it was an hour in which the Editor was doing nothing more vital than yawn at *Le Rire* and knock cigar-ash on the floor, he received the poet, and said:

"We are chock-ablock with poetry, but we might consider stories of a high order."

"At a high price?" inquired Tricotrin, replacing the "bouquet" in his pockets.

"They must, however, be in the latest mode. I suppose you have never visited London, hein?"

"But I have, monsieur! I spent a most edifying time in London. Why do you ask?"

"Our readers demand fiction generously decorated with colloquial English—we cannot *foot it* or drink *veesky-soda* too much in our feuilletons to please them nowadays; I have reflected that to lay the scene in London might exhilarate them more still. Is it in your power to evolve a story about English people?"

"On my head!" said the poet with secret dismay.

"And you can catch the veritable tone?"

"Absolutely! The hero will declare his passion on the golf-links, and the lady will reply, '*I love you; damn it, I am bunkered!*'"

"Very well, put your back into the effort, and if the result is realistic we will discuss a series. I do not say but what I might agree to accept one from you every week."

"Touching terms," murmured Tricotrin; "I presume, monsieur, that the remuneration is a louis apiece?"

"No," said the Editor. "To our favourite contributors it is ten francs. But in the present instance I could not pledge myself to pay so handsomely until I know whether your fiction is up to our standard."

"Have no misgiving," rejoined the applicant; "you will be ravished with it!" And though the absence of ready money was a drawback, he felt that the visit might have turned out worse.

Unfortunately the circumstances in which Tricotrin saw London had not conduced to an exhaustive knowledge of English life. The young man returned to the attic proposing to hammer out a tale before Pitou came in, but he found himself committed to a rebellious task. After an hour of labour he had produced no more than the following lines:

"Lolling in his luxurious *home* in the Tottenham Court road, the fashionable lord Bill Walker sipped a glass of rare *gin* and asked himself how he should pass the day."

This pleased the author by reason of its foreign words in italics, and its wealth of local colour, but he realised that it left him with little over. He was ambitious of referring intimately to the view beyond the fashionable lord's windows, but could not decide whether it was Hyde Park or the Thames. Continuing in desperation at last, he wrote:

"The view, so well known, on which his gaze indolently rested, a view that was even more *smart* than usual on this bright May morning, inspired him with no idea."

"What next?" muttered Tricotrin. " 'Inspired him with no idea!' He is in the same state as I am. Upon my word, it looks as if his idea will have to be to jump into the first train for Paris! But he would be travelling against the Editor's wishes, of course, so his trip would cost me ten francs. Peste! he is a sticker, this fellow—I always said the English were difficult to get on with."

By six o'clock he had lost all patience with his protagonist, who was still asking himself how to pass the day. Fleeing for inspiration to the streets, the unappreciated poet paced the boulevard with slow steps, reflecting, not for the first time, that Literature was an arduous profession. And, strange as the coincidence may appear, within a stone's throw of the Square d'Anvers he met the novelist, Lajeunie, similarly engaged.

"Dismiss your anxieties—you must not overwork! And let us talk about mine!" said Tricotrin, proceeding to do so.

"Well, well, probably a second-hand copy of a guide to London would settle your affair!" exclaimed Lajeunie, interrupting the recital. "To recur to my thirty-seventh chapter, which presents a weightier problem in psychology than any other chapter in my career——"

"A guide-book contains dryasdust details of Vestminster Abbey; lork Beel Valker cannot decide to pass his day in Vestminster Abbey, he is not that sort of chap. What I obviously require is the unmercenary collaboration of an English girl with blue eyes; a few of the prettiest English typists here could provide me with some tips beyond price, only they cannot express themselves in French, the donkeys. Be sympathetic! It is a tight corner I am in, and all for the lack of a nice little anglaise to take an interest in me."

"If you are indisposed to attend to my difficulties with Chapter XXXVII. I have no use for your company," announced Lajeunie. "Will you relieve me of the burden when I remind you that plenty of French girls can supply you with the tips? In the Galéries Lafayette, where, of course, I never buy anything, but where I occasionally take shelter from the rain, I have heard one of the assistants talking English as volubly as I have ever heard you talk rot."

"You don't exaggerate? A French girl who has lived in London? Why didn't you say so before? In what department is the treasure to be discovered?"

"If my memory serves me, the customers were inspecting waterproofs, Ask for the ladies' waterproof department, and keep your eyes open. You may identify her by a dimple in the right cheek if anything occurs to make her smile."

"The description is not redundant. Young?"

"A child of, say, three-and-twenty."

"Tall?"

"Not too tall to be caressable, nor so short that she lacks majesty."

"Blonde, or brunette?"

"A blonde, with exquisite ears."

"Pray heaven that my capital may suffice for her society!" cried Tricotrin. "If charm, and a bottle of beer will meet her views I see myself coruscating in *Le Demi-Mot* every week. I am off! Keep a brave heart, mon vieux; optimism whispers that your Chapter XXXVII. will turn out to be a gem."

Now whether the portrait had been idealised, or whether the beauty had had the sack, or whether Lajeunie had shamelessly invented her, with the object of continuing his promenade undisturbed, is a matter for conjecture. But Tricotrin could not find her. Vainly he scanned the features of all the employées in the ladies' waterproof department; not one resembling the majestic but caressable blonde with exquisite ears was to be discovered. In halting French, and with the thickest British accent at his command, he proceeded to ask if the establishment possessed an assistant qualified to attend upon an English customer. "But perfectly, monsieur!" An interval of vivid hope ensued. Then the bilinguous assistant appeared—in trousers. And not only was he disapponting in his sex, he was unpromisingly commercial in his manner. "Morbleu!" reflected the adventurer, with his jaw dropping. "For any suggestions that will emanate from this source lord Valker can remain in the Tottenham Court road till his second childhood."

The disappointing person demanded briskly what "mister desired."

Mister now desired chiefly to get out of the shop. Having observed a display of millinery far afield, he accordingly expressed an interest in millinery, with a view to eluding his conductor on the way to it. But suddenly something happened. A portly matron in the crowd, after regarding him with conflicting emotions, made a hurried movement towards him, exclaiming, "So it is you, you reprobate!" And, more disconcerted still, the young man found himself confronted by his aunt, madame Rigaud.

"My aunt!" he gasped. "What a joy to behold you again! And how is my beloved uncle?"

"I do not know that your uncle would at all approve of my greeting you!" sighed the matron. "You have repaid your dear uncle shamefully for his goodness to you."

"Alas!" said the culprit, who had long ago dismissed the incidents from his mind, "you tell me only what my conscience repeats in every hour. How astonishing it is to see you like this! You have not removed to Paris?"

"No, we go back to Lyons in a day or two. We have been in Paris a week; your cousin is with us—it was really on her account we came." She shook her head at him. "If your behaviour had been less scandalous we should have let you know of our arrival."

"It is a bitter thought that I owe the delight of meeting you only to chance," responded Tricotrin. And it did indeed depress him to reflect that he had lost a six-course dinner. "My cousin, the little Henriette! What an age since I saw that sweet child!"

"I hope I did not hear you inquiring for ladies' hats?" said madame Rigaud pointedly.

"I shall not disguise from you that that was the article. But do not wrong me by inferring that I am about to make a present; even if I had not outlived such follies, my pocket would exercise a restraining influence. I am engaged in the laudable and essential effort to turn an honest penny." To the interpreter, who was betraying considerable amazement at the fluent French falling from the "Englishman's" lips, he added in the latest slang of Montmartre, "Never mind, papa—hats are off! I'll look round your museum another day!"

"Behave yourself! What a way to talk to him! So you are as hard up as ever, hein? Your poems and plays have brought you no fortune, Gustave!"

"Your penetration is not at fault, my aunt. However, it is now too late to reform. Fervently as I may regret that I disregarded my family's counsel in the past"—even in his worst straits he had never regretted anything of the kind— "I am by this time écrivain for life, and the utmost that any one can do to relieve my sufferings is to supply some temporary assistance." The lady held a purse positively bulging with coin, and his gaze hung upon it fascinated.

"Well, well, unfortunate boy, I suppose you must go your way," she mumbled. But the purse remained shut.

"My way, this evening, is as far as your hotel, if I may have the privilege of escorting you," he declared, savouring a meal if nothing more. "Have you any other purchases to make?"

"No, I have got all I want. Well, let us go, then, if you are sure you can spare the time!"

"Providing, of course, that the poverty of my clothes will not embarrass you?" he questioned, in case she overlooked his need of a new suit.

"Your clothes will pass, my little one; I am not a woman of fashion. If one may ask, though, why do you wear so extraordinary a hat?"

"In the quarter where I live it is not extraordinary," he muttered, crestfallen. And they made for the door together.

"This Paris becomes more and more impossible!" complained the lady. "It demands the agility of an acrobat to cross a road."

"You need feel no trepidation while you are with *me*," said Tricotrin. It was not to hear her discourse upon the state of the traffic that he had proposed to accompany her, and he continued swiftly:

"I hope the hardships that an artistic career imposes on me do not distress you, my aunt? You must not grieve for me. I bear my trials with philosophy, remember! I am supported by the knowledge that your grandchildren will see a statue to me. Although I am often without food and fuel, I breakfast on brave hopes, and warm my hands before the 'sacred fire.'"

"Then you do not so fervently regret having rejected our counsel? Enfin, all the better!"

"Well, it is like this," he explained, confused. "For the sake of my relatives I do not regret—it will be something to have had Gustave Tricotrin in the family. But I feel that my fame will be posthumous—my constitution is failing, and I shall probably die young—and when I reflect that I shall not survive to wear the laurels, I confess that my courage wanes. Since I have had to choose between starvation and apostasy, there are moments when my interior wishes that I had been apostate."

"It is," she remarked, "these execrable auto-taxis that have done it—the chauffeurs behave as if they owned the earth! I do not know whether it is more dangerous now to walk or to drive—in one case you must expect to be run over, and in the other you woo a collision."

"It is very true," he assented irritably. "No, I would not have you grieve for me, my aunt! You must not let the remembrance of my privations torture you. Do not, I entreat you, condemn me to the thought that my dead mother's sister passes sleepless nights in recalling the extremities of my want!"

"To speak the truth, we ceased to worry about you a long time ago, Gustave," she said. "You turned your back on the opportunities that we offered you, and we realised that there was no more to be done."

"I am rejoiced!" said the bohemian blankly. And as his appetite improved with the stroll, it

was another and a heavier blow to him, when the
hotel was reached, to hear her say, "Alors, give
me your address! I cannot ask you to come in,
my boy—your uncle is so incensed against you."

"Mon Dieu! how heinous a fault is vindictive-
ness," moaned the forsaken poet on the pavement.
Through the basement window he had a tantalising
glimpse of cooks preparing purées. "What shattered hopes hail around me—all through the un-
initiative Valker! I know where he deserves to
'pass his day.'"

Herrings and lentils were a poor substitute for
an hotel dinner, and Pitou had all his work cut
out to offer solace. The plates were scraped before the harassed scribe would grant that a ray
of light was to be discerned in the request for his
address.

"And at the best," he said, "it will mean merely a snack, and a lecture! I do not foresee the
glimmer of a solitary louis; I do not anticipate
a forty-sous piece. If herrings were not scarce
these days, I would refuse an invitation by an
epigram in verse. Alas, hunger makes cravens of
us all! I fawned upon her, Nicolas, I cadged
like an ouvreuse. No, I deny it, it was not I—
it was my empty stomach! Shall a man be judged
by his stomach? But my heart and brain revolt
at the remembrance—my cheeks scorch at the
thought of the indignities to which I fell. I swear
that, with a square meal inside me, I had been
as high above them as the stars of heaven. Is

it not pitiful that a beefsteak may determine the difference between a hero and a cure.

But on the morrow, when the invitation arrived, his native buoyancy reasserted itself. Especially since Pitou, and Sanquereau, and Didier, and one or two other congenial spirits of the quartier opined that the silk manufacturer would present him with a bank-note to demonstrate that there was no ill-feeling.

"Should Crœsus hanker for a bust of himself, bear in mind that I am open to an offer!" bawled Sanquereau.

"Bring back to me a commission for a life-size portrait of thy aunt!" urged Didier.

"And pocket a slice of the fatted calf, that I may sup!" begged Pitou.

Rehearsing his features in an expression of ingratiating penitence, Tricotrin went forth.

Monsieur Rigaud, fully a stone stouter than when he had denounced the prodigal last, was spread in a basket-chair in the hotel hall. He tendered formal finger-tips, and growled. "So you have come, my fine fellow! You did not deserve that I should ever receive you again."

The visitor responded emotionally, "My uncle! Time seems to have stood still with you." And then, before either could say any more, there was a frou-frou of skirts and his astonished gaze beheld an apparition out of a novel. Advancing beside his aunt was a jeune fille with a complexion and a pair of eyes that made his senses spin.

"Your cousin, Henriette!" said madame Rigaud. And, dimpling demurely, the apparition touched him with a hand like a roseleaf and murmured, "Cousin Gustave!"

"Oh, I have expired and am in Paradise!" thought the stupefied poet, whose recollection of "Henriette" was a scraggy brat with a wisp of ribbon over each ear. The effect she produced on him was so sensational that moments passed before he became conscious that the manufacturer was in the midst of an harangue. Awakening to the fact with a start, however, he replied aptly, "All you say is, alas, true, my uncle! You honour me by this long-sought opportunity to utter my remorse."

"Humph! You owe it to your aunt's entreaties."

"How good of you, my aunt! You are both being far too magnanimous to me. . . . She has a foot to die under, her instep is an inspiration!" he reflected dizzily.

"I am well aware of our weakness," grunted the gentleman. "I am about to show you far too much consideration."

"Ah?" said Tricotrin, with budding interest.

"My judgment disapproves of what I am going to say."

"But your affectionate heart will not be quelled?" He fancied that the ingénue's lips flickered for an instant. Certainly her glance, which he caught this time, was not unsympathetic.

"Your uncle," began madame Rigaud, "has most generously decided, Gustave——"

"Permettez!" said her husband, interrupting her with dignity. "Mon enfant, I am informed—and I shall not pretend that it surprises me—that you remain a pauper. You may recall my predictions? Alors, while you persist in these fatuities I am not prepared to provide you with a sou——"

"Fatuities?"

"Poems!"

"Would it be satisfactory if I wrote comedies in prose?"

"Attention, imbecile! But I have been persuaded to allow you one chance more to amend your ways. For the last time I offer you a position in the business, and—enfin, if you are serious, if you content me, you will have prospects. You will have fine prospects. All is said. Now consider well, and give me your answer! If you accept, you will go with us to-morrow to Lyons. If you refuse, you may go elsewhere!"

How fatal to man's noblest resolutions is a susceptible heart! To say that scorn raged in Tricotrin is to put it inadequately. He had risen to his fullest stature; he tossed a dauntless head; his lips parted to spurn the mess of pottage, in burning words. But the enchantment of the complexion struck him dumb. To accept would mean to see her constantly! His intention tottered. The peak of Parnassus dwindled before her five-

feet-six of beauty. *"Jovis pater,* this is love!"
thought the poet, horror-stricken. And, flounder-
ing in temptation, he cried unto all the Muses
collectively to shield him against the barbs of
Cupid.

"Come, come, there is no doubt what his answer will be!" broke in madame Rigaud, taking
pity on his pallor; "he will make a very sensible
answer before he leaves us. In the meantime let
us take déjeuner, I beseech you, or the soup will
be cold!"

Never had the distracted young man contemplated so much food with so little enthusiasm.
His palate had fled and he masticated hors
d'œuvres like a machine. To sacrifice his career
for a woman? It would be sublime. But it would
also be frightful. One half of his mind yearned
to the romantic situation prodigiously; the other
opposed it with gigantic force. What a conflict!
With the soup, Literature fought like Carpentier;
but with the fish, you would have offered two to
one on the Complexion.

The maiden responsible for the terrific combat
helped herself to more sauce with the composure
of a deity.

"You find Henriette much altered, Gustave,
n'est ce pas?"

"But it is incredible, my aunt!"

"I am such a shock as all that?"

"Ah, mademoiselle! You are, if I may own
it, a revelation!"

Her eyes admitted that he might own it. Then she veiled them bashfully. "Too amiable, monsieur!" You would have offered three to one now.

Perspiration bespangled him. At last the host said a good thing:

"Again some wine, Gustave?"

"A very little, my uncle."

"Henriette, ma chérie, pass the bottle to thy cousin!"

Their fingers met. Literature was fighting tired, and the Complexion was as fresh as ever. He thought sonnets to it, and côtelettes de mouton à la jardinière might have been sawdust.

"I fear you have regarded me as one very obstinate and foolish?" he found a chance to falter while the parents were chasing gravy round their plates.

"Mais non! All the same, if I dared advise——"

"I implore you!"

"I would go to Lyons."

"A little gorgonzola, Gustave?"

Literature was on its last legs. Cheese found it staggering, and dessert saw it fall.

At the call of "coffee" it failed to rise.

Towards three o'clock that afternoon, Messieurs Sanquereau, Pitou, and Didier, taking the air on the boulevard de Rochechouart, were dismayed to perceive their comrade returning from the tents of the Philistines with the gait of a somnambulist.

"He bears no commission for a bust!" said Sanquereau heavily.

"My portrait of his aunt is another vanished prospect!" sighed the painter.

"That wretched Rigaud has not parted with a centime!" inferred Pitou.

Having realised their presence with a start, the poet drew them mutely to the terrace of a café. "Command what you will, my friends," he said, falling into a chair; "I shall give you a toast!" And he tossed ten great coins of five francs each on the table, scarcely noting where they dropped.

"Visions of splendour! Is he in the silver business now, your uncle?" queried Pitou, feasting his eyes.

"It came to me in gold; I changed it into silver to make it look more," Tricotrin explained. He raised his glass, and then, at the reckless words he uttered, three artists bounded so violently that they spilt good wine:

"To Hymen, god of marriage, and Gustave Tricotrin, manufacturer of silk!" he cried.

Minutes passed while the trio sat staring at him, speechless.

"The cousin!" ejaculated Pitou; "she is no longer so ugly as she was?"

"She was exquisite always," answered the lover indignantly; "you must be thinking of somebody else. But you have hit it. Yes, mes amis; I have seen the only girl I ever loved. She stands within the gates of commerce, but to clasp her as my bride I will endure all things, even employment. The degrading offer that you know of has been renewed—and to-morrow morning I go to Lyons."

"This is too hideous!" quavered Didier. "It is impossible that you are in earnest. Employment? Lyons? Oh, it is delirium! The offer was refused? Speak! Avow that it was refused."

"I go."

"Thou goest?"

"He goes!" wailed Pitou, recognising the symptoms of a great passion.

And that night it was said solemnly by many boys in Montmartre, "What a tragedy when a young man ruins himself for a pretty face! If youth but knew! Alas, one cannot put old heads on young shoulders!" It was a night of "good-byes," a night so poignant to Pitou that vale-dictory bocks well-nigh choked him. Dawn was breaking when the two young men wound their way back to their garret. The blank boulevard looked mournful, and the skies dropped tears.

"It has had its pathos," admitted Tricotrin, after a long reverie. "And the worst is still to come. It is leaving thee, Nicolas, that I funk."

"Without doubt I shall weep myself blind. And what then? The quartier without *thee*—I would rather not view it!"

"Ah, my quartier! the very rain is pattering memories this morning. The strangers that have blown here, to become our pals—and the pals that have flitted, to be seen no more. One by one we vanish. Last year 'twas Goujaud—now 'tis I! Listen, thou dost not go to the station with me.''

''Bien!''

''I could not bear to part from thee in a crowd.''

''I understand. Yet I could have wished to learn how She looks. There is one thing I have not said, Gustave—I bear her no ill-will, although she takes thee from me.''

''I was sure of it.''

''To be practical, thy trunk will not contain a third of thy manuscripts.''

''It will not contain one of them; they belong to my past!'' replied the new man firmly. ''If thou wilt, keep them in remembrance of hopes that we have shared.''

Neither of the pair slept a wink.

''I have left twenty francs for thee on the wash-handstand, Nicolas.''

''I duly noted them—thou wilt find them in thy hat. I should feel as if I had sold thee!''

''Sentimentalist! One cannot argue, then,'' sighed Tricotrin, cording the box. And in lieu of arguing, he surreptitiously transferred the coins to the other's tobacco-pouch.

There were a hundred and sixty-four stairs to descend, and every one of them was bad for the heart.

Monsieur, madame, and mademoiselle Rigaud were alighting from a cab as he reached the station. "Little you surmise what ploughshares I have trodden to win you!" thought her victim, greeting the girl while her father disputed with the driver, and her mother screamed agitated instructions about bonnet-boxes. In the atmosphere of excitement created by the Rigauds, père and mère, on their way to the booking-office, he had the impression of being swept to his doom on a whirlwind.

Their places were selected, and their wraps and impedimenta and refreshments disposed to their satisfaction at last. Madame fanned herself with a newspaper, and withdrew a little mirror and other articles from her sac-à-main, to repair the ravages of travel. The manufacturer, puffing achievement, clasped his hands over his fancy waistcoat with the air of one who had been around the world in thirty-five days. The ingénue retired modestly behind a copy of L'Illustration. And the engine whooshed.

By an effort nothing short of superhuman the Parisian refrained from throwing himself on to the line.

Baffling are the vagaries of the poetic mind! It may have been that the maiden displayed undue interest in L'Illustration, or it may have been that his thoughts had been dwelling more persistently on Montmartre than on the maiden; but some time later, when his uncle quitted the compartment to smoke a cigarette, her adorer himself was capable of detachment from the loadstone of her presence. Crœsus and the exile smoked in the corridor together.

"It will be no misfortune to sleep in my own bed again!" observed monsieur Rigaud, who had recovered his composure. "It is not for amusement that one undertakes such journeys."

"Business before all things!" responded the young man laudably. "I wager you have made a bit by the trip, my uncle?"

"It is true. I do not complain on that score. Not that it was an affair of the firm—it was an arrangement more intimate." He was confidential. "You have heard of monsieur Duchambon, the advocate?"

"No."

"No? *Mais!* Monsieur Armel Duchambon? He is a young man most distinguished! It would not astonish me to see him President one day. He is very well born, too; his parents are very proud—it was not many families at Le Touquet that they consented to know; it was at Le Touquet that our acquaintance with them began. Enfin, it is now settled! I am conscious that they have squeezed from me a larger dowry than they had the right to exact, but, on the other hand, I have forced the Duchambons to pull out nearly double the sum that they had determined to give their son. Your cousin marries monsieur Armel Duchambon, and I am well content."

"Henriette," gibbered Tricotrin, "is affianced to another?"

"Another? No, to Duchambon, as I say."

"But—sacré tonnerre! For what, then, do you imagine I forsook my art?" demanded Tricotrin indignantly. "For the insufferable silk and a vulgar prosperity? A thousand 'noes'! It was for *her*—Because I Loved Her!"

At these words, spoken with that simple, manly feeling that one may hear on many a stage, the senior's face turned so rich a purple that several passengers in the corridor forgot their cigarettes to survey him. His throat appeared to be too tight for his expletives; and the train slackening at a platform, he suddenly turned and shoved his nephew in the chest.

"*Insolent!* Return to your art!" he spluttered.

"Alas! I have no money to take me. Control yourself! You have registered my luggage through to Lyons."

"I snap my fingers at it! . . . Tenez, it is the last sou of mine you ever see in your life—here is enough for a third-class fare! Get off the train!"

"I should have expected sympathy, not reproaches," said the poet with dignity. "However, I make but one request. You will permit me to see her for the last time?"

"Get off the train!" roared the manufacturer, dancing with resentment, and he hustled him through the door.

As the familiar footstep sounded on the stair—
But you will divine that Pitou "paled" and
"sprang"; you may have read something like that
situation elsewhere.

"And the ticket left me with no change out of
his wretched dole!" concluded Tricotrin; "I come
back stone-broke, and without my trunk. . . . I
suppose it would be preposterous to inquire
whether any remnants of that twenty francs linger here, after eight hours?"

"What will you?" said Pitou. "In appeasing
the general desolation, the final centime was disbursed by half-past three."

"It is good to be missed so much!" exclaimed
the poet thankfully. "Besides, our pen will provide. Is there not always lord Beel Valker?"

V

The Woman in the Book

SOME fifteen years prior to the creation of Lord Bill Walker there dwelt in the dull town of Viroflay (Aisne) a poor girl named Toine, the daughter of a concierge. A concierge is a superfluity fostered in France to extort tips and invent scandal. Toine had a charming countenance, a voice that urged her to warble as she hung up the washing, and an inconstant disposition. She enlivened the tedium of her lot in Viroflay (Aisne) by love affairs with Bazaud, the tailor's son, and Durand, son of the tobacconist, having previously yielded her maiden heart to Lebobe with the blonde curls, who was heir to all the stylish hats and costumes in The Ladies' Paradise. Then, when the poor girl was eighteen, the concierge removed from Viroflay (Aisne) to extort tips and invent scandal in Paris; and Toine attended free classes for the stage, and called herself "Toine Viroflay." Viroflay (Aisne) scoffed that "the theatres of Paris could get along all right without that Toine," and remarked that she would have been wiser to stick to the washing. . . .

What became of her progenitor is forgotten, but

Toine rose from the lodge of a concierge to a sumptuous first floor, and had manicured hands, and an automobile. When she had been notorious in Paris just long enough for her to begin to consider face massage as well, she even played for a season in London, where she received so much kind hospitality that the sensational experience of finding herself a guest in respectable houses positively palled upon her. By this time, Bazaud, Durand, and Lebobe were middle-aged men and reigned in their fathers' stead. Bazaud had a wife and offspring now, and Durand was a widower; and Lebobe, who had not married—it was difficult, he explained, for one with all those stylish hats and costumes at his command to credit disinterested affection—had nothing left of his curls but a bit of fluff over his ears. When they read, in the Café de la Mairie, after their shops were shut, of the Parisian celebrity's "priceless sables," or the superb emeralds that had been presented to her by a prince, each of the three stout provincial tradesmen would nod at the newspaper weightily, and think of the epoch when he himself had elated her by the gift of a ribbon. "Life is droll!" said Bazaud, Durand, and Lebobe.

Now, one spring a theatrical rival of Toine's was moved to issue her autobiography, and it promptly occurred to Toine that the world should be favoured with her own. She mentioned the idea to the Editor of *La Voix*, and he thought so well of it that he proposed to run her work through his

journal with innumerable portraits. She wrung
from him a contract such as his most distinguished
literary contributors had never viewed even in
their blithest dreams; and it would have been all
smooth sailing with her plan, but for the fact that
she was no more capable of writing an autobiography than of constructing a submarine.

When a few months had passed, she received a
deferential note from the gentleman inquiring at
what date he might be privileged to behold her
masterpiece. And not having done any of it, she
invited him to pay her a visit.

She said, "You know, a most fascinating volume is in my mind, but I need some one to spare
me the fatigue of preparing it for print."

The Editor was not one of those high-minded
editors who would perish rather than deceive their
readers—he wasn't an Anglo-Saxon. He cared
not a tinker's expletive who wrote the costly manuscript, so long as the public accepted it as Toine
Viroflay's and he got good value for his money.
Therefore he replied in tones of syrup:

"But perfectly, mademoiselle! It would be in
the highest degree absurd that you should concern
your artistic head with details like that. To provide the 'copy' there are professional authors—
and such things can be employed for next to
nothing."

"Well, call one, as you go back," drawled Toine,
"and tell him to be round in half an hour."

And, returning to the office, the Editor found

on his door-step a poor poet, of the name of Gustave Tricotrin.

"We are not buying poetry," said the Editor, "so waste no time in unpacking your wares. But I might put something in your way that you would find more lucrative. I should not wonder if it proved to be worth a couple of hundred francs to you, if you could do me a narrative of about eighty thousand words full of snap."

Whereupon he proceeded to be confidential.

"What an insult!" said the poet furiously. "You refuse my epics at the rate for shaving paper, and ask me to boom your rotten rag by permitting an actress to steal the kudos for my brains. The offer is an outrage." He said this to himself, however; aloud he said, "It is extremely amiable of you to think of me in the matter, monsieur."

So, after Toine had broken three appointments, he had the honour of an interview with her on the sumptuous first floor.

Despite his resentment of the circumstances, an interview with a star was by no means an unwelcome event in the obscure bohemian's life. And though Toine ordered authors as less eminent persons order cabs, it was not in her nature to talk disagreeably to a good-looking young man while he behaved himself.

"I do not doubt that I shall be well content with your aid, monsieur," she told him.

"Rest assured, mademoiselle," he responded,

"that my poor talents are wholly at your service;
your experiences shall be set forth with all the
literary skill at my command. In fine, I shall
aspire to hear Paris exclaim that mademoiselle
Viroflay writes nearly as well as she acts."

"Or even quite as well!" said Toine.

"You would not need to be a madame de Staël
to do that!" thought he. For it must be confessed that she did not owe her position primarily
either to her vocal or her histrionic powers. And
he went on, "As to the valuable material that you
will supply—your early memories, the treasured
recollections of your childhood, the first throbbing
of ambition? If I may venture to suggest it, the
best way would be for you to inform me of as
much as possible this afternoon, and to spare a
few minutes to me daily till you have given me an
outline of the rest."

"*Comment?*" screamed Toine. "Daily? Mais
—mon Dieu! Do you figure yourself I have nothing to think about but a silly old book? Ah, zut,
alors! I understood that you designed to save
me all the bother?"

"I do, I will," stammered the scribe, dismayed;
"it will be a rare joy to me! Only . . . I feel
sure, mademoiselle, that on reflection you will
perceive that I should be made acquainted with
the facts that I am to record? I shall mould them,
I shall embellish them; I shall pose them in the
most alluring attitudes with rosebuds in their
hair; but to accomplish your autobiography, I

truly fear that I must possess somewhat more than the universal knowledge that you are transcendently triumphant, and gifted, and beautiful."

"Ah, well!" she said, open to reason. "What is it you want to know?"

"Well, to begin with, mademoiselle, may I inquire whether you are Parisienne by birth?"

"No; I was born in the provinces—a loathsome spot it was!"

"Your parents, were they also in the theatrical profession?"

"Not they! But you can leave my parents out; the book is to be about *me*."

"Understood! It may suffice if we mention that you were a 'devoted daughter.' Before we arrive at your first engagement, though, we should afford the reader a glimpse of your girlish life; some homely scene, bathed in atmosphere. The more rural, the better! I think of the contrast between misty meadows and effulgent fame. You grasp the idea?"

"Ah, mais écoutez, donc!" she cried; "you may afford the reader what you please, but do not ask me to recall any homely scene! I tell you I detested the hole, and all its stupid crew; I bless the day that I got out of it. . . . No, what we shall do is this—I shall lend you my album of press cuttings. It will show you what parts I have played, and what the critics have said of me in them. And one day, I will tell you some anecdotes, extremely sensational, of great personages

I have known; also many infamous things that I
have suffered at the hands of jealous col-
leagues of both sexes. As for the rest, monsieur,
I leave it to you. I am convinced you will manage
it very nicely and my autobiography will be all
that it ought to be. Some afternoon, when I have
leisure, you shall come again and read a few
pages. Now I must entreat your pardon—it is
the hour for my drive.'' She yielded soft fingers,
and smiled coaxingly. ''Don't be long finishing
the job, I supplicate—time presses!''

''It appears that I am committed to an exhaustive work of fiction!'' mused the discomfited poet
on the staircase. ''What an undertaking for two
hundred francs! It is colossal. Certainly my
heroine has a captivating appearance, but fiction
is more exigent than life—in fiction a woman's
appearance is not enough. Mademoiselle Toine
has no fine attributes, no spiritual graces—she is
devoid of almost everything essential to a heroine; I have got to invent a nature for her, as well
as a history! . . . I wonder how much space her
anecdotes will fill?''

Mounting to his garret, he drew a chair to the
table; and having dipped his pen in the ink in-
dustriously, sat staring with despondence over the
chimney-pots.

''What piece of work are you at now?'' demanded Pitou, re-entering at nightfall.

''I have been entrusted with a task which I am
not at liberty to communicate,'' said the poet.

"However, you may see as much of it as I have done." And he displayed a blank sheet of paper.

It was not till the morrow that he decided on Toine's nature. Then he resolved that she should be a woman whose genius had thrust her into notoriety against the dictates of a simple heart. And this being determined, he got along with her treasured recollections at a fair pace. Her passing reference to the "dear father and mother, who were not spared to see me conquer," could hardly have been more wistful within the compass of twenty words; and the line in which she hinted at present-day reveries by their tomb was replete with tenderness.

"By disposition I am domesticated," she declared further on. "Even sweeter music to my ears than the plaudits of my beloved public—that says something!—are the voices of children at play. Ah, the little innocents! How often, in a brief respite from a feverish career, I have gazed wide-eyed at some smiling peasant in a cottage doorway, her babe upon her breast! You ask me what emotion the sight inspires in me? It is envy. Yes, I avow it! I question whether I would not change places with this humble woman, in whose vocabulary the word 'art' does not exist, but whose modest joys are to me so unattainable, so eloquent, and so sublime."

At this point the poet lit a cigarette to re-consider his adjectives. His heroine was coming out better than he had expected; he began to take more

interest in her. On the night that he approached
the period of her struggles to gain the first rung
of the ladder it was with compassion for the sufferings that he was about to inflict upon the poor
child.

Toine, too, approved of herself thinking holy
thoughts by the cottage door, when the scene was
read to her. This time Tricotrin found her less
uncongenial; after endowing her with fine qualities for eight hours a day for a month, it was not
the easiest thing to remember continuously in
her appealing presence that she did not possess
any of them. Moreover, her approval led her to
comment that the scene was "very true—it is extraordinary how you understand me!" When the
moment for her drive came, he regretted it. This
afternoon the touch of her soft fingers was distinctly pleasing.

His heroine, rebuffed by all the managers, was
a pathetic figure. Her dauntless hope amid the
interesting calamities that befell her was not less
moving than the warm sympathy that she extended
to the luckless of her profession when laurels had
been won at last. Beneath a crown her head remained of the same circumference as it had been
when she was en cheveux. That was, perhaps,
the virtue that endeared her to him most. Flat-
tered and fêted, she retained all the ingenuous
spontaneity of her teens—and broke an engagement with a Grand Duke to bear comfort to an
ailing ballet-girl.

The actress approved herself in that incident as well, when she heard of it. She put on a deprecating air and murmured, "It comes near to being a fact, by the way; you are more than littérateur, monsieur—you are magician!" And now he had been endowing her with fine qualities every day for two months—and to the artist's fervour the Toine of actuality was confused so much with the Toine of his figment that he sought excuses soon to call on her again.

So the poet, in his attic, made for her a heart out of his own feeling, and a mind out of his own ideals, and created for the woman the soul that she lacked. And the woman, in her vanity, tried to appear to the poet like the queen that he had achieved.

And then, when he wrote, his heroine smiled, in his fancy, with the real woman's face; and when he went to her rooms, the real woman was glorified, in his illusion, with his heroine's thoughts. And he fell in love—with the goddess of his book, and imagined it was with the wanton.

And socially, of course, a successful wanton was as high above a mere man of letters as the white moon of heaven. He confessed his sentiments to her only when he was asleep—and woke, terrified by his presumption, before he had had her answer. That is to say, he did not get any further than this until a good many weeks had passed.

"You have no regret, mademoiselle, that you confided the work to me?" he faltered one day, when not a great deal more remained for him to do.

"But quite the reverse!" she exclaimed. "How do you come to ask such a thing? You have tackled the job with inspiration."

"The inspiration was my protagonist. I ask because—because—— Enfin, it is because I wish the result to content my employer, at any rate."

"You are not content, yourself? . . . Ah, I understand. The true artist is never wholly content with his performance. It is the same with me."

"No, that is not it," said Tricotrin, whose nervousness became more apparent every minute. "It is from personal considerations that I often feel that it would have been discreet of me to let the chance slide. . . . I shall be frank! I acknowledge that the offer was welcome, that in my poverty the fee was not to be sneezed at. But, if my purse was slim, my wants were few; hard up as I was, mademoiselle, I had one blessing that I would not have bartered for a fee far greater— and the job has stripped me of it!"

"Tiens?" she said innocently, reclining on a couch. "What may it have been?" Her gown, though then the very newest thing, was like that robe the lissome Vivien wore, at Merlin's feet in good King Arthur's reign—it "more expressed than hid her" where she lay.

"It was my peace of mind," explained the poet. "Ah! when you so lightly hired me, did it not

occur to you to wonder what emotions must beset
the poor devil whose days were to be passed com-
muning with you, on paper, in your every mood—
dwelling beside you, in spirit, in your every hour?
To write your Memoirs was to comprehend you,
and to comprehend was to worship—I am the most
miserable of men!''

Toine's instinct was to burst out laughing, but
she recognised that this would not suit the great-
hearted heroine that was her latest rôle. So she
murmured with mournful intensity:

''How you have distressed me! What grief
your confession brings! I had not an idea—I
have always thought you viewed me purely as a
theme. Mon pauvre ami, I shall never pardon
myself what I have done. Ah, mon Dieu, it is not
all candy and cake to be a woman!''

The poet's impulse was to bound with elation
at her taking it so gently, but he realised that as
a suitor he should be prostrate at her implied lack
of responsiveness. So he groaned, with a gesture
of despair:

''I am no more to you than your lackey!''

''What you have said is cruel,'' she expostulated, doing her utmost to sound wounded to the
core. ''I have not deserved that at your hands.
For one thing, I have a vivid admiration of your
artistry; and for another, the artist has become
a friend.''

''But—I am illimitably honoured, but . . .
Ah!'' he cried, falling on his knees, ''be merciful!

If I have climbed in a few months to the pinnacle of your friendship, am I mad to dream that in time I might soar to the empyrean of your love? Grant me the hope, and I will wait in silence. I will be patient; I will be enduring. My submission alone shall plead for me!"

"As to that," she conceded, since silent hope would prove no nuisance, ". . . who shall divine the future?"

"Ah, the thought of time is torment! I adore you to-day!"

"Do not persist—you may see that I suffer!"

"There is only you in my world!"

"Everything you add increases my self-reproach."

"I expire at your feet!"

"Enough, I entreat you—your pain is insupportable to me!"

"Toine! With a word you can end it!"

She was in a pass that she had been wishful to avoid. She paused, seeking for the heroine's way out. When she spoke, her tones were deep and grave:

"With a word I can end it? . . . Yes, it is a fact. And, since I have spoken that word to men who were as shadows to me, you mean that there exists nothing to prevent my speaking it to you, a friend? I understand. You tell me that if I permit your misery to continue, it can be only because I am callous to it? Ah, unhappy one that I am, I have not the right to resent that

taunt! . . . I wonder if *you* will understand *me*
when I say that it is because I am far from callous
—because I have for you a sentiment which no
other man has wakened in me—that I cannot sham
to you? I cannot! All that is highest in me protests. The passion that you crave may yet be
born, but—I cannot feign it. To you I would
yield nothing but the unsullied truth. Ah, my
poet, you, who have seen behind the mask, who
know me as I am, do not ask me to sink below
the Toine you love! Do not ask me to profane
the purest affection of my meretricious life! To
others, to the world I can be courtesan, but to you
I would be myself."

The poet was deeply affected; his speech in
reply was on a plane no less lofty than her own.
And now, buoyant with the hope that his love
would be reciprocated yet, he accomplished such
flights of fancy with his pen that his heroine was
exalted to more celestial qualities on every page.

As the bulk of the manuscript was already delivered, the Editor at this juncture decided to
start publishing it. I Avow All, By Toine Viroflay, was announced on every hoarding. And if
Paris was not precisely duped, it was at all events
much tickled. In the cafés, waiters grew tired of
informing customers that "La Voix was engaged"; and the orders that reached the office
from the provinces showed that interest in the
Memoirs extended beyond the capital.

In Viroflay (Aisne), however, the interest was

not acute prior to an instalment which contained the following paragraph:

"The dear public spoil me; the lavish gifts that rain upon me daily are amazing. Yet diverted, dizzied as I am by all that there is the most rare, I recall—I shall never forget—one gift that was made to me years ago. Would you hear what it was, that unique present? It was a rag doll, of the value of a few sous! Who blessed me with it I know not at this date, but assuredly it was some poor creature who could ill afford the price. I ask myself how it fares with such humble bene-factors of my piteous childhood—those kindly, careworn souls among whom I passed my infantile years, and whom my best efforts have failed to trace. I pray that Time has dealt gently with them!"

The one-eyed widow who sold papers in the kiosk at the corner of the rue des Missionnaires alighted on the paragraph first, and she observed to the femme de ménage of the charcutier, "After all, she is the right sort, la Viroflay—how fondly she alludes to the folk who were nice to her here! It is not everybody who remains so grateful in prosperity." And after a pause, she added, "I had always a soft spot in my heart for that little one—it was I who gave her that rag doll!"

The femme de ménage mentioned the paragraph to the wife of the hump-backed cobbler; and the cobbler's wife, speaking of it to the good woman at the gates of the Octroi, said, "How clearly I call her to mind, la petite—somehow she attached herself to me. It was from me that she had that rag doll, you know!'' and the woman at the Octroi, gossiping with the crone from the booking office at the railway station, remarked, ''As if it was only last week I remember her face when I took that rag doll to her—her delight was so pretty to see!''

These three boasts developed into that epistolary siege by which it appeared to Toine that every female among the population of Viroflay (Aisne) claimed to be the donor of a rag doll that had not existed, and begged for financial relief. She did not trouble her head with any of the letters in particular, but in the mass they were exasperating, and she wished that the poet had not invented a rag doll for her. She excused herself from listening to a new chapter at this period; she felt unequal just then to sustaining the heroine's immutable amiability.

Her impatience wronged the town; if she had read the letters through, she would have known that showers of them were from contemporaries who scorned to lie about the rag doll. Each of these reminded her that the writer had been her twin soul when they were at the Free School together, and having detailed monetary anxieties, remained ''Your old friend who loves you ever.''

The autobiography was now widely discussed in Viroflay (Aisne). In the Café de la Mairie, Bazaud, Durand, and Lebobe severally scanned the journal, over their evening bocks; and a few weeks later, as luck would have it, they scanned a copy of an issue wherein the heroine was in her most domestic mood. Thus:

"And now, now that those struggles so stupendous are past—now that my aspirations have been fulfilled—am I content? You are going to tell me that I should be thankless otherwise. But my sole purpose in writing these Memoirs is to blurt forth the truth—and I avow that often I mourn! In many hours of solitude I question if Fate had not been gentler to withhold my triumphs, and even my talents—to permit me to dwell obscurely in the sphere that I forsook. Through my tears I see again a young girl—poor; yet rich in the possession of a brave man's love; and I tell myself that this love of her youth was a vaster treasure, though she knew it not, than all the splendours that she has since attained. One must suffer to grow wise! It is too late. But fairer far, in my reveries, than bouquets that symbol fame, is a little knot of field flowers that a brave man gathered for a girlish breast one long-gone Easter morn."

"*Comment?*" ejaculated Bazaud, Durand, and Lebobe, jumping in turn; "she loves me still!" And though none of them had any definite recollection of an Easter morn, each added to himself, expanding with pride, "Without doubt, it was jolly well I who gathered those field flowers!"

Needless to say, not one of them had made a

secret of his dynasty; and so, that week, each of
the trio observed pompously to the others, "Mon
Dieu, I am touched! It makes me reproach myself
that I did not fathom her devotion for me at the
time." And each of the others replied, with a
fine smile, "You distress yourself without cause,
old chap—what she says refers to *me*. The 'knot
of field flowers' puts it beyond dispute, for I
vividly remember the incident."

The discussion grew heated; and at midnight,
when the three tradesmen left the café and went
their respective roads, "What conceited fools they
are, those two!" soliloquised Bazaud, Durand,
and Lebobe.

Now, all the way home, monsieur Bazaud,
though a family man, was lured by visions of a
gilded scene in which he should sit, for a while,
with the great woman who was still sweet on him,
recalling the days of yore. What a tremendous
adventure! The idea trilled in his bosom. And
all the way home, monsieur Durand, who was a
widower, fluttered at the breathless notion of
sentimental dalliance for a whole week amid the
celebrity's grandeurs. It would be as a week of
royalty! And all the way home, monsieur Lebobe, who had remained a bachelor from scepti-
cism of being loved for his qualities alone, palpi-
tated before a prospect vaster yet; he questioned
whether he might not do worse for himself than
give his name to the opulent queen of the stage
who adored him.

That night Lebobe wooed sleep in vain. And he regretted much that the exigencies of business —they were stocktaking at The Ladies' Paradise —made it impossible for him to indulge in a trip to Paris before the following week. That she might be speedily apprised that he was "touched," however, he telegraphed to her on the morrow. Toine found further food for disapproval of the poet's fancy, when she received, with the Editor's apologies for having inadvertently opened it, a telegram from Viroflay (Aisne) which ran: *"I have read, and I have wept. Time has stolen my curls, but it cannot impair my tenderness."* In a temper, she tore it into as many pieces as she could manage. "Ah, c'est trop fort!" she cried. "I am fed up with Viroflay (Aisne)!"

However, there was nothing to postpone the trip in the case of Durand. He was shaved, and trimmed, and frizzed, and had his moustache curled; and he embarked on his enterprise with a posy in his buttonhole. And when she was accosted at her porte cochère by an ardent tobacconist in his Sunday clothes, who brought a grin to the face of her chauffeur, Toine's temper boiled higher still.

Durand returned from the enterprise with no illusion about the lady's sentiments for him. And now, incensed by the thought that either Bazaud or Lebobe must be the lucky man, he burned to put a spoke in the wheels of both. Lebobe, as a bachelor, was beyond his spite; but he contrived

a word in the ear of madame Bazaud. And since
Bazaud had been artfully paving his way to a
solitary excursion, the young woman believed the
worst and was broken-hearted. She wrote distractedly to her mother in Paris.

The advent of a persistent mother without a
bonnet was even more trying to Toine than the
arrival of the Sundayfied tobacconist. Her rage
knew literally no bounds at this mortifying appeal
to her not to poach on the preserves of the tailor's
wife. And when her contempt for the snip was
discredited, and she heard herself reviled in the
most expressive argot for ensnaring his affections, she felt it to be the limit.

She was reckoning without Lebobe. No sooner
was the stocktaking concluded than Lebobe hied
him to the metropolis with a bulky valise and
lively anticipations. The interval had served to
strengthen his view that to propose marriage to
her would not be throwing himself away, in circumstances. But it would be a noble course—and
he foresaw with pleasure her emotions at his chiv-
alry. At the office of *La Voix* he demanded her
address with the bearing of one who had no
doubts about his welcome.

They were irritating at the office with their
insistence that they had mademoiselle Viroflay's
injunctions to withhold her address from everybody. However, at a café table a directory was
to be consulted. From the nearest bureau de
poste he despatched a pneu to advise her of his

arrival; and then he visited a barber's and had the most made of the fluff over his ears. When he mounted to the flat, his step was brisk.

Now, the pneu had not been delivered yet; and it happened that at about this hour Toine was expecting Tricotrin, to present the final chapter of his manuscript, and a photographer, further to perpetuate her beauty. When Lebobe inquired authoritatively, "Mademoiselle Viroflay, is she at home—I have an appointment?" the new Bretonne maid took him for the photographer. For that matter, Toine herself took him for the photographer as he was shown in, and she wondered where his camera was.

"Ah, you have come, monsieur," she yawned. "Is your assistant with you?"

"My assistant?" said Lebobe blankly. "How, my assistant? . . . Do you not recognise me? Have the years, then, changed me so much?"

"Oh, mon Dieu!" she moaned in consternation. "Another!"

"I am your Achille, your Achille of other days. You received my message? . . . Toine? You know me now?"

"Yes . . . I was expecting some one else. I know you."

"My curls have vanished, hein? Such is life! You also have changed; but for the better; you are not so thin. I should have known you anywhere. . . . How it comes back, the past! I am touched. You may see that I am profoundly touched!"

"Listen, monsieur," she said, quivering with annoyance; "it was very amiable of you to pay me a visit, but I am much occupied and I cannot prolong the reminiscences."

"*Comment donc?*" exclaimed Lebobe. "Ah, you do not comprehend my motive! It is to see you that I am in Paris; I have things to say to you of the first importance. Ever since I read your tender words in *La Voix* I have thought; I have thought very attentively; and I am here to repeat that you spoke for us both! To me, too, time has proved that prosperity is trivial, compared with claims of the heart; I, too, would exchange the profits that The Ladies' Paradise has yielded to revive those field flowers of that Easter morn. We were boy and girl; in those days there, we did not realise the eternal force of our affinity. What you wrote was *bien* true, of me no less than of yourself. I avow it with contrition. I avow with contrition that I was terribly culpable towards you from the start. But despair not, my Toine well-beloved! Where your reflections were at fault, where you made an error—it was in thinking that it is now too late!"

"So that is it? You have come to console me for my loss of you?" she muttered in a strange voice.

"I have come to make amends. I have come to say to you, 'In my youth I committed a great wrong and I would atone.' I have come to say, 'You are the woman that I adore—and I ask you to be my wife!' "

She stood speechless. Her indignation at the audacity was so overwhelming that she could not articulate. She tottered like a dumb woman demented.

"Have no misgiving!" proceeded Lebobe magnanimously; "I do not speak on impulse; I know well what I am about. For your infidelities in the meantime no reproach shall ever pass my lips. Indeed, they were not infidelities, those things— they were but efforts to forget me."

"*Espèce d'idiot!*" she panted.

"You say?" croaked Lebobe, petrified.

"Insolent imbecile!" Her advance was tumultuous; he backed from her in jerks. As often as her volubility—for she was now very voluble indeed—permitted him to make himself heard, he put in agitatedly, "I regret, I regret! Do not get excited—it was your Memoirs that misled me!" But every allusion to her Memoirs seemed to excite her more; and, interposing his hat at the most dangerous moments, he continued to back about the room till he was breathless. The sudden announcement of a visitor, affording an opportunity for escape, looked a dispensation of Providence to him.

Not so to the visitor, who was the poet responsible for the Memoirs. He entered to reap the whirlwind of her resentment—to see the final chapter hurled to the floor.

"It is to you, little liar, that I am indebted for these pests!" she cried furiously. "It was not enough that you smothered me under begging let-ters from every mendicant in France?—that you conjured up enamoured tobacconists to make me ludicrous on the pavement, and the mothers-in-law of tailors to belabour me with abuse? You must also see to it that this rag-tag and bob-tail arrive with offers of matrimony? Alors, I owe your imagination more than I can pay! But take your two hundred francs, and be off, and never dare to set foot in my flat again!"

"Mon Dieu!" he gasped; "I lose my senses. What have I done? Explain, I implore! It can-not be you who speak. My world turns topsy-turvy—I was the one who knew you best, and on a sudden I know you not at all! Do you not see your friend, your worshipper?"

"I see only the fool poet who wrote my auto-biography and muddled me up in a hornet's nest!"

"This is not you! It is not you!" he wailed, be-wildered.

"It is *bien* I, and I am tired of being somebody else! Your heroine fatigues me."

"I begin to understand," said Tricotrin, as one who wakens from a dream. . . . "Yes; it was only the fool poet who wrote that beautiful auto-biography; but it is the woman herself who has written 'THE END'! . . . I go. In parting from her whom I have loved so well, may I be granted one fleeting touch?''

"Oh, if you like!" she said roughly. She put out a grudging hand.

But he bent, instead, to the manuscript and held it for a moment in his arms.

VI

The Piece of Sugar

THEY say that the poor sirens of the little
cafés frequent them for three years, and vanish. For three years they haunt the same scene
nightly—now bold, with their paltry trinkets; now
desperate, with their trinkets pawned—prinking
to the fiddles of the sham Tziganes. Then ominously they disappear. And the glasses still rattle
in the incurious crowd, and the fiddlers fiddle on.

So, from more brilliant scenes, women whose
spell lasts longer, and whose jewels are the gifts
of kings, may disappear. Corinne Blanche had
disappeared. Already she was ancient history. A
decade had slid by since heads turned after her
famous horses in the Bois, and royal personages,
going to Paris, booked a box just to look at Corinne Blanche. Great ladies who had copied her
toilets recalled them now as "those fashions that
were so absurb." Middle-aged men might say, "In
the epoch of Corinne Blanche"; their juniors, listening to stories of the fortunes that had been
lavished on her, and the deaths that lay at her
door, might reflect that life must have been more
spectacular when they were boys; but the name

of the slender girl whose career had scandalised two continents was no more than an echo.

And then, one October evening, a provincial, visiting Paris, turned into a café of the least pretensions, and gathered an experience that lingered with him all his days.

This fortnight's holiday was a treat that Emile Richard had long promised to himself. It provided his first opportunity to see more of the capital than was to be beheld during the brief excursions that he had made to it in the company of his parents. On quitting the lycée where he had been educated, his father's office in Lyons had claimed him, and since then it was only during the term of his military service that he spent so much as a day away from home. To stand in the streets of Paris free to penetrate its mysteries, had been his aspiration ever since he read Balzac. In fancy, a hundred adventures had happened to him under its lamps, and on the afternoon when his long-cherished project was fulfilled at last, when he hastened from an hotel into the vivacity of the Boulevard, conscious that a whole fortnight of potentialities stretched before him, he had swung his cane in a transport of anticipation.

Young Richard was of the French middle class, and his character was not Southern—in other words, he was mean. The prodigality of the exotic, and the improvidence of the bohemian were as foreign to his nature as the habits and customs of the Martians. Although he was on pleas-

ure bent, his frugal mind retained a just appreciation of the value of the sou, and his transports
were soon damped by the discovery that his daily
expenditure was exceeding the sum assigned for
it. Of course he could dip more deeply into his
savings, but he wanted to accomplish his plan at
precisely the price arranged. He began to perpend before he opened his little purse now. He
went to the Eldorado, because it was cheaper than
the Folies-Bergère, and ceased to order vin supé-
rieur, at an additional charge of fifty centimes,
with his luncheon.

When half his holiday was over, Richard's pro-
nouncement upon Paris was unfavourable. He
could not credit it with having unfolded a single
mystery. He was, on the contrary, chagrined to
recognise that he had viewed nothing but the
obvious, and seen only the exterior of that. In a
ferment, he put on his dress-clothes, and walked
swiftly to a supper restaurant where he had noted
white-gloved men and resplendent woman alighting from automobiles at midnight as he passed.
But on reaching the glow of the doorway, he was
reminded that they were visible on the sidewalk
too, and that his supper there would probably run
away with a couple of louis. He vacillated, holding his breath. Inside, to be sure, the women
would take off their cloaks. But two louis!

"It is not what I seek," said Richard, backing;
"that also would be the obvious! No, what I

squander two louis on must be something that
every stranger cannot see!''

Paris was a greater ''fraud'' than ever as he
returned to the hotel through the long emptiness
of the rue de Rivoli. He was disgusted with Balzac.

Presently it occurred to him that there was a
fellow in Lyons with some slight knowledge of an
out-at-elbows poet here; an out-at-elbows poet
should be able to serve as guide to the resorts of
the humbler artists. Even a glimpse of those
might be more interesting than the monotony of
trudging between the Madeleine and the Porte
St. Denis all day. Of course, there was the risk
of his trying to borrow money, but one could be
cautious—one could make use of him for an occasion, and cut the acquaintance short! Richard
resolved to drop a line to Lyons and try to ascertain the poet's address.

His deferential note, conveying the assurance
of his ''distinguished sentiments,'' reached Tricotrin's attic a few mornings later. The unappreciated composer who occupied the second bed had
recently secured an order to copy band parts,
while the threadbare poet was at this period the
authority who, under the pseudonym of ''Monsieur le Duc,'' instructed male readers of *La Voix
Parisienne* how to attire themselves in accordance
with the last word of fashion.

''Ma foi, I seem to savour a singularly pleasant
evening!'' he exclaimed, perusing the graceful

lines. "He writes from an hotel where he must
be blowing four or five francs a night, even if he
is on the top floor. Evidently it is a wealthy chap
who desires to call on me. We shall certainly
consent to be known, mon vieux! I wager that we
get a thundering good dinner."

"It will cost us something, too," objected Pitou;
"you do not propose to receive him in a garret?
And if we give him a rendezvous at a brasserie we
shall have to inquire what he will take to drink.
He may say 'veesky-soda,' a man in that position."

"I admit that it will make a hole in our coffers;
there will be a few preliminary beverages, I do not
doubt, and we shall have to pay for some of them.
But we can entertain him during an afternoon at
the cost of a trifle—a hundred sous should suffice
to give us a lavish air—and at the dinner-hour we
shall be repaid with interest, voyons! It would
not surprise me if he invited us to a music-hall
afterwards. All the same, it is as you like, do not
let me commit you to the investment against your
will."

"I was wrong: your view is sound," agreed
Pitou. "We can run to fifty sous apiece, if we
reduce our déjeuners during the following week.
Besides, when the symphonic poem that I am
making of your *Chaos* is accepted we shall both
be flush. If you knew more of music, you would
rave about what I am doing."

"I know more of music than you think," said Tricotrin, who knew nothing of it whatever.

"Slightly different from the *Chaos* of Haydn! I put no key signature, nor time signature, nor do I suggest in what keys the transposing instruments should play."

"Not bad. But is it not a shade conventional?" objected the poet, at a venture.

"Conventional?" screamed the Futurist. "That I should share a bedroom with such a benighted heathen! Get on; reply to your millionaire! It is a partnership."

At five o'clock on a sunny afternoon, then, behold the pair arriving at the little Café du Bel Avenir in an expectant frame of mind. The appointment had been made for 4.30, but in France, of course, "4.30" means anything from five o'clock to six.

"Madame," said Tricotrin, putting his head in at the door, "a monsieur, to whom I am not known by sight, will be inquiring for me." And they took chairs on the "terrace," which was about as long as a small dining-room table, and ordered a couple of bocks, which they allowed to stand before them untasted.

Not more than twenty minutes had elapsed when a very spruce young gentleman in patent leather shoes was to be seen approaching. He glanced at the name on the awning, cast a questioning eye at the two comrades, and entered.

"This is our man," murmured Pitou, "I much fear."

"Do not leap to conclusions," said the poet; "he may have an expansive heart, though he has an unpromising physiognomy. Yes, here he comes!"

"Monsieur Tricotrin?" inquired the stranger, bending at the waist, and holding his hat at his hip. "I am ravished by the honour of making your acquaintance, monsieur."

"Monsieur Richard? Rejoiced to have the opportunity of greeting you! I am desolated to have put you to the inconvenience of coming so far. Permit that I present my friend! monsieur Pitou, the composer—monsieur Richard."

"Ravished!" repeated Richard, with another bow.

"Enchanted!" responded Pitou, saluting with equal ceremony.

"Will you not sit down, monsieur? What may I offer you?"

"Ah! . . . I thank you infinitely. Alors, if you insist, a bock!"

"You prefer it to anything else? Garçon, a bock for monsieur! Yes, I fear the neighbourhood was somewhat remote for you, but the exigencies of my work are such that had I suggested a rendezvous on the Boulevard, circumstances might have prevented my turning up in time. Here, I am at home, you understand; I can run round in a moment!"

"But it is perfect!" affirmed Richard urbanely,

regarding the dilapidated side street as if it had
been a beauty spot in Paradise. "My delight at
finding myself in the society of you gentlemen is
intensified by the fact that I am also introduced
to a quartier which is new to me, and so extremely
pleasurable."

"It is your first visit to Paris, monsieur?"
asked Pitou.

"Ah, non, monsieur! But I avow to you that
it is my first opportunity here to promenade at
my ease. Hitherto my business has always been
paramount; for the first time, I am tourist, sight-
seer."

"And there is enough to look at—it is not a bad
little town," smiled Tricotrin, "hein?"

"There are beautiful buildings," acknowledged
Richard, in the tone of one who is anxious to do
no injustice. "And it is larger than Lyons."

"A shade! It is also more interesting, n'est ce
pas?"

"In a sense, ah yes—we have not the Louvre in
Lyons, we have not your Opéra. Nevertheless I
shall own that, with me, Paris has not lived up to
its reputation. It is only this afternoon, in the
company of a poet and of a composer, that I am
precisely fascinated." His thoughts were, "As
a matter of fact, all I discover so far is two shabby
young men, and a fifth-rate café—there is nothing
epoch-making about that!"

"Ah, too amiable, monsieur!" said the twain in

a duet. And, inclined to think more favourably of him, Tricotrin went on:

"It is the artistic side that attracts you most, then?"

"Voilà!"

"So much the better! You have struck the right spot. Montmartre is the brain of the capital."

"Really?" murmured Richard, surveying the dirty little street again and trying to look more impressed by it still. "I regret that I do not know my way about; doubtless there are many scenes that I should have found captivating."

"But if you would care to take a stroll——?"

"That would not be inconvenient to you?"

"Not the least in the world!"

"How amiable you are! I should be enchanted. But I am embarrassed—I am overwhelmed by your consideration!"

Whereupon they strolled, and came to a larger café.

"What may I offer you?" inquired Pitou.

"Ah, but I impose on your hospitality, I am not come to rob you," demurred Richard. "Well—er—again a bock!"

"This place," explained Tricotrin with an enthusiasm that was perfectly sincere, "is no less celebrated hereabouts than the Café de la Paix down there! One might say it is the 'Centre of the Quartier.' You may see here men whose names a few years hence will be household words to all Paris." He meant to the "whole of the civilised globe," but as he was a Parisian "all Paris," in such a sense, signified all outlying districts of less consequence as well. "You may see philosophers pondering great truths; composers, perhaps scoring a phrase on the back of the tariff; painters, who behold with their mind's eye canvases that will be accepted as masterpieces of modern art."

"Tiens!" said Richard perfunctorily. What he discerned was a crowd of nondescripts sipping drinks and rustling evening papers. "I foresee that our walk will be a succession of thrills."

"Round the corner," added Pitou, "there is a tavern where the customers are theatricals; after the shows, many of the players from the theatres close by drop in there for a plate of onion soup. The chatter is all of the stage—it is like being in a green-room. We will have a look at it in a minute—sometimes a few go there before the shows begin. Ah! there are half a hundred haunts, each with its special clientèle. There is one whose feature is the singers from the music-halls, where one hears all the scandal of the Casino, or the Gaîeté. There are two favoured by the feminists; and others by the apaches of both sexes; and there is one where you would see the apostles of a new religion. Midnight is the best time for that, but it would be well worth your while. The women are extraordinary."

"Ah?" said Richard. "I should have no objec-

tion, I am not in any hurry to get back. Let us
go there at midnight, if you will be so complai-
sant? I would not mind looking at the apaches
either. There is no danger?"

"None at all. Right! It is agreed. Finish your
drink, and we will make a move! For messieurs
les apaches we have a little walk in front of us.
Mon Dieu! it is a programme, hein? Before you
sleep you will have become a veritable Montmar-
trois!"

The theatrical resort when they reached it
proved somnolently disappointing. And though
the faces of the apaches were criminal enough to
proclaim them the genuine article, it was not en-
thralling to watch the weedy little scoundrels play
cards with two of their repulsive-looking "lady
friends." At half-past seven, when the trio
emerged from the den, Richard was partially sus-
tained by the fact that he had been allowed to pay
for nothing but a packet of Maryland cigarettes,
but he meditated irritably that this gleam of satisfaction would be extinct if he were now committed to paying for a couple of dinners in addition to his own. Conversation languished. Econ-
omy urged him to bid his guides an effusive au
revoir. On the other hand, there was the chance
that they themselves would burst forth with a
proposal to dine—and he was reluctant to miss
the café of the new religion.

The glances exchanged between the poet and
composer became anxious. They had expended

five francs seventy-five on his entertainment, and
for upwards of a quarter-of-an-hour they had been
waiting, with enormous appetites, for an allusion
to their reward.

Before half of the boulevard de la Chapelle had
been retraced, their hearts were on the way to
their boots. The glances grew more eloquent still,
and at last, with a galvanic jump, Pitou ejaculated—

"Mon Dieu, I had forgotten! We were to dine
at Lajeunie's to-night! We are too late!"

"Morbleu!" gasped Tricotrin, seizing the cue,
"it had slipped my mind! What an offence—
the anniversary of his wedding too!"

"Ah? You have broken an engagement through
me? Quel malheur! I am contrite, I shall never
pardon myself!" cried Richard.

"Ah, I pray you! It is not so catastrophic as
all that. But it is incredible; it is the first time in
my life that such a thing happens to me. Voilà,
a testimonial to the charm of your society! Enfin
. . . we shall send a telegram; do not let the little
contretemps spoil our evening."

"But . . . I am distressed, I have no words!
All my joy is ruined, I shall reproach myself as
long as I live!"

"I assure you! Believe me, it makes no matter," insisted Pitou. "Indeed, we shall pass the
hours more agreeably as it is. We can invent an
adequate excuse. Finished! There is but one

question that seems to concern us now—where shall we all feed?"

"I do not know the neighbourhood, I," regretted the tourist helplessly; "to me it is all the same. Where you will! It is for you to choose."

Again the eyes of the comrades met with apprehension. The vital question was, who was to be the host?

They were pale as they steered their way to a table in a modest restaurant. "Ah! I beg you to excuse me for an instant," stammered Tricotrin, rising almost as he sat down; "I should telephone my apologies to our friend!"

"I, too!" declared Pitou, stumbling after him.

"What do you think, is he going to pay?" they asked each other, in a panic and the lavatory. And then, counting their cash so nervously that a ten-sous piece nearly dropped down a basin, "Have we got enough, if the worst comes to the worst?"

"Well, we can manage it if we choose the dinner at three francs," groaned Tricotrin when they had done fumbling. "But what an outrage, after our preceding munificence! It is unheard of! Oh, it cannot be! It is impossible that he will permit us to fork out here too—he would never have the nerve."

"Generosity is not infectious; a mean nature can accept it all the year round without developing reciprocal symptoms," said Pitou. "If I were confident that he would 'never have the nerve' I

would take good care that we dined à la carte.
Why cannot the dull dog manifest his intentions?
. . . Alors, let us keep away for a few moments
longer, perhaps he will give the order while we
are gone!''

And Richard, in the meanwhile, was saying to
himself, with folded hands, ''You will find me
awaiting your return, my dear conspirators! In-
contestably it was the invitation of the other side.
That they were only fishing for one from me is
their trouble. Also it is cheaper for two persons
to pay for one guest than for one person to pay
for two! What they have shown me was not worth
the cigarettes, of which they have smoked the
greater part. Zut! I am the right man to be
taken in by their humbug about the engagement
they had forgotten. I shall stand some coffee
later on—it will be quite enough.''

How ironical a stroke, that the only member of
the party to relish the repast was the one to whom
a dinner of five courses was no novelty! His intentions had become manifest only too soon, and
the poor bohemians, to whom the meal looked
epicurean, could hardly taste their food for swal-
lowing their indignation. The bill-of-fare swam
before their gaze. Between the efforts of making
civil responses to their guest they regarded him
with vindictive eyes.

''Sapristi! If bohemia is not exactly staggering in other respects, it overwhelms me with its
hospitality,'' he declared, plying an indefatigable

knife. "May I trouble you for the pepper, monsieur?"

"Certainly, monsieur," said Tricotrin morosely. "Take it all! So bohemia is not exactly staggering, hein? And in what way does the little village of Paris fall short of Lyons?"

"I do not go so far as to assert that it falls short of Lyons——"

"Too generous!" muttered Pitou.

"But it falls short of the representations that are made for it. In literature, and even in your newspapers, it is pretended that Paris teems with as many adventures as 'The Thousand-And-One Nights.' Well? In Lyons also we have criminals, though we do not go to stare at them! The ladies of the new religion may perhaps reveal some original phase, but up to now—during the twelve days that I have passed here—frankly, I have come across nothing of human interest that I could not have viewed elsewhere. There has not occurred to me a single experience to make me cry, 'Ah! this is extraordinary—I have disbursed a little fortune on my trip, it is true, but I have encountered something that could not have happened to me at home.' On the surface the life is suggestive enough, but on investigation it is commonplace; in fine, it lacks the quality of which it boasts so much —drama. Now let me make up my mind what cheese I am going to have!"

"Your criticism, monsieur," returned Pitou,

"may be sound to the core. But all the world disagrees with it."

"Ah, flûte! What does it mean 'all the world'? Veritably it means 'the average man.' Well, the average man persuades himself that he is looking at what he wants to see! Ever since he was a child he has been stuffed with the old accounts of Paris —when he comes here he arrives with his opinions ready-made. My friends, the glamour of Paris is, five-eighths reflections from the romances we read in our boyhood; a quarter the produce of our own imagination—and the remainder, Paris! I shall take camembert."

When they sought their hats, the poet whispered to the musician, "He is appreciative, this gentleman who has nearly cleaned us out! Let us give him a doing if he is not willing to show us his purse!" And each taking Richard by the arm, they set forth from the restaurant at a lively pace.

By the time that he had been bustled from the boulevard Barbès, up the acclivity of the rue Lepic, as far as the heights of the Moulin de la Galette, the tourist, whose patent-leather shoes were beginning to pinch, assumd that the objective was attained; he asked, "What is that that I see?"

"Ah! a ball-room of sorts—commonplace!" answered Tricotrin disdainfully. "What I aim at displaying to you is Old Montmartre. It is disappearing so fast that this may be your only opportunity to look at it." And they continued to climb into a Cimmerian maze that threatened to be everlasting.

"You do not find it a trifle cheerless?" panted Richard. "The municipality are not too extravagant with lamps, hein?"

"That, I confess, is a drawback," said Pitou; "at this hour there is the risk of receiving a stab in the back. But from where we stand, the view of Paris was superb some years ago, before they began to build."

"We arrive some years too late to see it, however," mumbled the other apprehensively. "I venture to think that the ball-room might have been more amusing?"

"Commonplace, I assure you!" repeated Tricotrin. "Patience! After a few more ups and downs, we shall behold The Nimble Rabbit. Besides, the assassinations here are comparatively rare." And at last, when another sinister hill had been scaled, and a decayed auberge shed a feeble glimmer in the blackness of the desolation, he cried heartily, "There it is! This is an off night for it, so we shan't go in, but you are viewing something historical. It has had a rare vogue, The Nimble Rabbit."

It was past eleven when the victim was allowed to limp to more populous regions; and he puffed, "If we go in somewhere—if we take a coffee or something? Really, you must relax your hospitality—we are in bohemia, and I claim the bohemian licence; this time *I* shall be the host!"

How could he suspect that, after bocks were commanded, the deceitful pair would feign to descry an acquaintance in the half-empty brasserie and come back, with long faces, to announce that the café of the new religion had been closed by the police?

"*Comment?* Then I have waited all the evening for nothing?" he faltered.

"Alas!" sighed Tricotrin.

"Too bad!" growled Pitou, dissembling a grin of malice.

Richard fingered his glass moodily. From his heart he regretted that he had not taken leave of them after yawning at the dull apaches; the free dinner did not compensate for its disgusting sequel. Surreptitiously he removed his shoes. The artists, wearing an air of woeful disappointment, pressed each other's knees with satisfaction. All three gazed before them in protracted silence.

And then something happened—a real and arresting thing, eminently Parisian. A lonely woman in soiled satin was sitting at a long marble table, with her back to them. In her audacious hat were cheap plumes, and in her little bag were a mirror, and a stick of lip salve; twice in ten minutes she withdrew them and, without the least concealment from those in front, made her mouth still more grotesquely red. No one else was at the table but a stout man, who pored over *Le Soir,* and sipped a liqueur of brandy; the customary piece of sugar that had been served with it

lay neglected. To the woman had been supplied a
"ballon blond." The presence of poor women
like her stimulated business in the café, and they
were privileged to order one low-priced consom-
mation without payment. Sometimes they were
too hard up to pay if they had wished. She of
the plumes was too hard up to-night.

The stout man finished his liqueur and went.
The woman sat alone, and her back was despond-
ent. Next, the group behind her saw her throw a
hurried glance to either side; her little bag was
opened furtively—and the painted pauper with
the plumes and satin stole a piece of sugar for her
wretched home.

The annoyed provincial lost sight of his vexa-
tion. As for the artists, the incident quivered
through them. Simultaneously they turned towards each other.

"Mon Dieu!" breathed Richard. "What a
life!" He leant across to Tricotrin. "What a
life, hein?"

But now Tricotrin was motionless, with his
mouth open; as if by a sudden misgiving, the
woman had looked round and he had seen her face.
When he did speak, it was in tones studiously
quiet, though the cigarette that he rolled was
shaking.

"In Paris one runs across nothing dramatic,"
he drawled, with a fine smile. "Nevertheless the
poor devil who has come down to pilfering a piece
of sugar for her next day's coffee, once played

ducks and drakes with the finances of a king. She
is Corinne Blanche!''

The thrill that Richard craved had come! All
that the name evoked to them, all of the profuse,
the fantastic, and sensational that they had read
or heard of Corinne Blanche in the days of her
empire swirled through three men's minds.

''Impossible!'' fluttered Pitou.

''I say what I know. It is Corinne Blanche.
A woman who has scattered, not one fortune, but
a score! A mere million was nothing to her, it is
said; she could gobble a banker before breakfast;
for love of her a prince died. And to-night she
sits in a third-class tavern, companionless, and
steals a piece of sugar for the morrow! Though
there is nothing dramatic to be remarked in Paris,
I, who am a dramatist, find that not uninteresting.''

''It is colossal,'' admitted Richard. ''I avow
it; it is colossal!''

The littérateur was on his feet, an impulsive
hand among the remaining sous in his trouser
pocket:

''If you will pardon my deserting you, I shall
go and talk with her! It may be of value to my
work.''

''Sit still!'' expostulated Pitou. ''How? Do
you figure yourself that she is going to recount
her history?''

''I comprehend perfectly,'' said Richard, ''I!

Let all of us talk with her! It would be extremely pleasant to me."

"Ah, for us all to look so keen would come expensive!" demurred the poet with a scowl. "It might commit you to champagne," he added artfully.

"And then?" persisted Richard, reckless at last; "I should not be unwilling to order a bottle of champagne. After all, it is something, to entertain a woman who has mocked herself of monarchs."

"Well, I will see how it goes—I will give you the tip," said Tricotrin, in a hurry to be gone. And betaking himself to the chair at her side, he sat down.

It diverted them to watch him make some opening remark and to imagine a mechanical smile. But when four or five minutes had lagged by they began to grow restless.

"He forgets all about us!" grumbled Richard.

"I shall jog his memory," said Pitou, to whom "champagne" had sounded excellent.

He began to flip matches at Tricotrin, and the hint served. They saw him indicate their table inquiringly now. To Richard's delight, the woman rose.

She was no longer pretty, and no longer young; and, as she approached, the brilliance of kohl could not hide the tragedy in her eyes. But the tragedy itself possessed a morbid fascination for him. It was fascinating, when he bowed, to hear her voice and to reflect that, not so long ago, there had been men who shot themselves because that voice had sent them packing.

Yes, the emotion that he had sought was found. And because nothing happens but the unforeseen, it had been found when he least expected it. He addressed himself to her continuously, with hardly a twinge for the ever-mounting expense, though she uttered nothing but trivialities, and it had transpired that she would like a little supper. Neither Pitou nor Tricotrin was allowed to gain her ear for ten consecutive seconds. More and more they were excluded by his elbow. It was Richard's hour! They indemnified themselves with the viands and wine, falling to with such a will that almost as often as he made to refresh her glass he discovered the bottle to be empty, and the waiter was kept busy drawing corks.

Not until the bill had been called for, and his jaw had dropped at the total, did he accord the young men his attention. He said:

"Messieurs, I would not hasten your own departure, but she is fatigued, and it appears that she lives some distance off: I have offered to drive her home. I thank you a thousand times, both! This day that we have passed together has been superb, altogether ravishing. . . . And listen!" He buttonholed them, to be confidential: "I shall yet obtain her reminiscences! You will not find me neglect you—I shall write you things, hein? . . . You remain?"

"A few moments—there is still something left to drink," answered the pair. And as Richard strutted forth beside her, Pitou collapsed against Tricotrin, panting hysterically:

"What inspiration may be born of a piece of sugar!"

"Inevitable!" gasped the author, half-voiceless with laughter, too. "She had scarcely sneaked it when I thought to myself, 'To make that more literary still you should be some woman with a dazzling past!'"

"For an instant you took *me* in. You knew why I said you would not get her history? That was in case he should smell a rat when she was not autobiographical. What did you say to her?"

"I said," quavered Tricotrin suffocatingly, "I said, 'Madame, we have a country cousin there who thinks you were the favourite of emperors; I have ascertained that he will run to champagne, and I should not wonder if you could raise oysters as well.' Oh! it was a gallant deed. The poor ancient lady, whoever she is, has had probably the best supper of her lowly life, and our wiles have cost that scurvy knave a hundred and two francs already!" Mirth rolled him on the settee till he clasped his stomach in pain. "He means to pester for her 'reminiscences,'" he shrilled. "Oh, I would give a hemisphere to see his face when she loses patience with him and he learns what he has spent the money on!"

VII

The Banquets of Kiki

PARIS steamed, and Parisians mopped their heads; and Kiki Toulotte panted to spend her approaching birthday at Saint-Cloud among birds and boughs. If the student of these chronicles imagines that because Kiki was a model of scant importance she could not yearn for birds and boughs in true poetic style, the student wrongs her race; even a French girl shambling down the rue de Flandres at six o'clock from the jam manufactory where she works may be heard to speak of the one glimpse she has had of Fontainebleau—yes, and of a landscape on the walls of the Salon!—with some spontaneous phrase of feeling that is poetry in itself. Kiki felt lyrical.

Unhappily, the coins that she could count fell very short of the sum required. For it would be a poor sort of birthday if she went alone. She wanted to provide a hamper of cold meats and bottles, and bask in the company of monsieur Tricotrin, who, much to her regret, had never made love to her; and she wanted to invite his friend Pitou, and her own pal, Louison-Flore, to whom the composer had dedicated unpublished serenades until that terrible affair last month when he bade her farewell for ever. Was it not evident to half an eye that both would jump at a reconciliation? Could Kiki's sentiment have had its way, indeed, the party would have lunched on the shady terrace of a restaurant. And it would not even run to the hamper!

NOTE: This superficially appealing situation should not be allowed to enlist the student's sympathies for the young female. Sentiment and poetic yearnings are not necessarily concomitants of a high moral standard, as will become sadly apparent.

Now the café that Kiki most affected of an evening was called the "Joyous Jackdaw," and its clientèle, if not prosperous, was sprightly, especially about midnight. Not only were artists' models to be discovered there, forgetting their anxieties—there were beauteous beings from the chorus of a neighbouring music-hall, who had been known to chant over their bocks from sheer lightness of disposition. Many a blade of limited means maintained that more "life" was to be seen at the "Joyous Jackdaw" than at any other café in the quartier for coppers. But of course these were habitués; a stranger who dropped in there was liable to find it dearer. A week antecedent to the dawn of Kiki's birthday, a stranger from the suburbs found it dearer—in the following circumstances.

Some people may remember, and it is of no importance if they don't, that in the suburb of Ville-Nogent there stood a pension de famille presided over by a crimson-faced woman of vast dimensions? She was an avaricious termagant of the name of "Grospiron," and her husband, whose days were spent behind the wire screen of the local branch of the Crédit Lyonnais, was a niggardly little fellow who, to avoid the expense of cutting a slice of bread for himself, would make a tour of the dining-room table and collect the bits left by the boarders.

The couple saved money. Almost the only matter that they discussed together without the irascible woman raising her voice was the amount that they had saved. She it was who was the more consistent of the two. In spite of his domestic parsimonies, in spite of his official deliberation—and the time he took to supply a draft on London had never been exceeded in any bank in France—Grospiron was, at long intervals, subject to secret frolics, on which, in the most reckless of his moods, he had dissipated nearly a louis. Ville-Nogent was not an animated spot, and once in every twelvemonth his accumulated cravings to escape from it would be more than he could master. At Christmas he used to pretend to his wife that the stress of balancing the accounts kept him at the bank until one o'clock in the morning. Had she suspected that he slunk into the 7.15 to

Paris, and rushed from glittering scenes to catch
the last train home, she would have struck him.

Long years before, when the clerk had been
transferred to Ville-Nogent and drifted for
"board residence" to the house over which he
now nominally reigned, the vast, crimson-faced
woman had been a plump, rosy girl, who received
resounding clouts from a violent mother. To-day
the intimidated Grospiron often mourned the
touch of a vanished hand.

The little man's annual lie had, as it were, become hallowed by custom. It was now easily
uttered, and smoothly accepted. Never had he
adventured it at any other season than the one
in which the actual pressure of work lent an air
of credibility to his tale; never for more than a
febrile instant had he dared to contemplate such
a thing. But accidents happen in the best regu-
lated sins. One August morning, into the rue de
la Paroisse came a white-bloused fellow with a
paste-pot; and through the bank window the
meagre clerk beheld him slap on to the hoarding
opposite, a picture of a disturbing damsel, in
three sections, and a tango posture. Grospiron's
dual mind skipped from the figures he was totting
to the floor of the Bal Tabarin. He reproved
himself, and cast the last column again. When
he had done so, his gaze involuntarily roved to
the calendar, and he sighed in realising the procession of dates that had to pass before the appearance of Christmas.

Strange as it may sound, Grospiron grew restless during the ensuing week. As often as he raised his head, the hussy on the hoarding was reminding him that he could be borne to Paris in forty minutes, and attain the merriment of the ball-room at the end of half an hour's palpitating stroll. In fancy he pushed open the swing doors and quivered. Constantly he dismissed the notion "for good and all"—only to look up and see the highly coloured siren beckoning to him again. When she had been on the hoarding for ten days, his fever had mounted to the degree of considering how to dupe his wife in August.

Four days more passed while he sought courage to execute the plan. Then he murmured tentatively that owing to the absence of a colleague he might have to put in an hour or two overtime on the morrow. Next, as she did not protest vehemently, he moaned that it wouldn't surprise him if it proved to be a "really late job."

When she had swallowed the yarn with no more than a choleric "Mais!" he wished that he had said "this evening" instead.

How far was every one from divining the tumult in his veins next morning! Externally he was as deliberate as ever, and when the oldest client of the branch presented a cheque payable to "Self," Grospiron's meticulous examination of it was so prolonged that he seemed to be at the point of charging the client with having forged his own name.

In the deceiver's purse were fifteen francs.
Not without a pang had he put them there to
be scattered, but after vacillating during two-
thirds of the night he had determined that fifteen francs should be the sum. The afternoon
pulsed with promise. At seven o'clock he sidled
towards the station, and as the woman in the
booking-office slid out his return ticket he held his
head warily above her view.

In the corner of a compartment he consulted
the current time-table and confirmed his conviction that the last train for Ville-Nogent left at
12.30. When Paris was reached, he made assurance doubly sure by inquiring of two officials,
and set his nickel watch by the station clock.

"Ah!" said Grospiron to himself with boundless satisfaction, hastening down the steps.

How good the shining streets looked! How
exhilarating was the movement of the crowds!
He twirled his little moustache excitedly, and was
scant of breath with pleasure.

As usual, the temptations of a myriad enter-
tainments confused him as he walked; as usual,
before proceeding to Tabarin, he was beset by a
desire to venture a franc or two upon some new
experience, and then hesitated in the fear that
when he got to the ballroom all the chairs would
be engaged. "Moulin Rouge," "Jardin de Paris,"
"L'Alcazar," a thousand glittering signs dizzied
and delayed him. . . . Since he had had no dinner, he would be bound to order a snack at some

period of the evening! He resolved to have a sandwich and a glass of beer at once. While he discussed them he could make up his mind.

Pleasure was giving place to anxiety, as it always did. As on every previous occasion, his brain buzzed in the consciousness that an experiment might ruin the whole spree. On the other hand, what visions of delight he might be missing! . . . "Ah!" he exclaimed again, with the torrent of significance with which a Frenchman can flood the monosyllable, and made impetuously for the Alcazar.

When he had paid for admission, and treated himself to a programme, and found that he could neither see nor hear much of the entertainment, his regret was riotous. Continuously lamenting that he had come, but reluctant to abandon a seat that had cost him one franc fifty, he fumed and fidgeted till half-past nine. Then he strode to Tabarin at such a pace that by the time the rue Victor-Massé was attained he felt that the ladies of the cloak-room might have wrung him out like something from a wash-tub.

Luck was against him still. The doors that had been swinging in his imagination for the past fortnight disclosed an almost empty scene.

"Mon Dieu," groaned Grospiron, "the night fails!" His despair was accentuated by a view of gala baubles, suspended from the ceiling and intimating what high jinks were to be expected on the following Saturday.

Gulping a bock, and dabbing himself with his handkerchief he eyed the few gyrating couples morosely. So deep was his chagrin during the ensuing hour that not even the brief appearance of a troupe of paid danseuses could stir him to applause.

"Where is the tango artiste that one sees advertised on the walls?" he demanded angrily of a waiter. And, the waiter proving obtuse, a lady explained, with a smile, "It is not an artiste, monsieur, it is a symbol."

"It is not a symbol, it is a fraud!" growled Grospiron, disconcerted. "I am bored here."

"It was jolly last night," said the lady, by way of comfort.

She suggested taking refreshment in his company, and sat down. Far short as she fell of the tango witch, she was some one to talk to, and his gloom lifted a little by degrees. He was sorry when, her glass being empty, she rose to express an intention of going to the Joyous Jackdaw.

"What is it, the Joyous Jackdaw?" he asked, pricking his ears.

She replied that it was a café, and that he should make its acquaintance. "It is amusing!"

"And expensive?"

"Oh, quite the reverse!"

Grospiron was agog to take her tip. But did time remain? At twelve sharp he must set forth for the station. He consulted his watch.

"How long will it take to get there?"

"Not two minutes!"

"I am with you!" he proclaimed debonairly. And as he strutted round corners beside her he felt that he was penetrating the mysteries of Paris at last.

On entering the café he was a little dashed at her discovering two of her friends, for she cordially invited them to drink at his expense. They were Kiki Toulotte and Louison-Flore. Their mien was moody at the moment of the introduction, for Kiki had been dwelling on the impracticability of her birthday party, and Louison-Flore was pondering upon Pitou. Both cheered up wonderfully, however, when the lady extended her invitation to the length of hard-boiled eggs.

"Hard-boiled eggs also!" assented Grospiron, slapping the table. The spurt of festivity had occurred too late to make the evening a success, but, sapristi! it should yield him one gay memory.

And no quartette in the café was more vivacious. Laughter pealed, and his spirits rose so high that he did no more than wince when it transpired that the prices were 50 per cent. more than they ought to be. His consuming care was that he was bound to flee at midnight. Again he looked at his watch, and was agreeably surprised to find that it was only twenty-five minutes past eleven.

"He is like Cinderella!" cried Kiki amid general mirth.

"Still more like the Prince!" thought Grospiron as he saw himself committed to cigarettes. But

he forced a boisterous air, and, reckless in the
possession of his return ticket, practically emptied
his little purse.

It was when half the packet of cigarettes had
been smoked that he pulled out his watch again—
and stared at it with his blood running cold. It
stood at twenty-five minutes past eleven still!
Paralysed with fear he questioned how long ago
it had stopped.

"The time?" he gasped, starting to his feet.
"Mon Dieu, my train! Garçon, the right time?"

"A quarter past twelve, monsieur," announced
the waiter as if it didn't matter in the least.

The little man turned grey to the lips. Unless
he took an auto-taxi to the station, there was no
possibility of his reaching home before the milk.
An auto-taxi—and nothing remained to him but
coppers!

"Ladies, ladies," he babbled in a panic, "my
train goes at 12.30. It is the last! I need an
auto-taxi; I have not the money! Lend it me,
I implore you, I entreat you on my knees! It is
a situation the most desperate. I am a gentleman, I live at Ville-Nogent, my name is Grospiron
—I confide all to you. I will repay you to-morrow
—to-morrow, on my honour! Three francs for
a cab, I supplicate! It is life or death to me."

His excitement did not communicate itself to
his guests.

"Ah, par exemple!" objected his guide, with

the calmest of shrugs. "Three francs! I regret
infinitely."

"Then you, mademoiselle?" he panted, pre-
cipitating himself towards Louison-Flore.

"Alas! I am not a millionairess, monsieur!"
said she.

"I will pay interest, I will give security, I will
do anything," he besought, his knees clacking
together. "Mademoiselle Kiki? For the love of
heaven, have you three francs?"

"Well, yes, I have it," admitted Kiki, "but
ma foi! c'est un peu fort—we are not the oldest of
friends. People don't do such things."

"I will pay five—ten! As security I offer—I
offer my watch!"

"Which doesn't go!"

"It is a good watch," he shrilled, with a sob;
"it is the first time it plays me such a trick. Ah,
come to my rescue! I will give you an IOU. Be
compassionate, be quick—any second may be
fatal!"

Now the prospect of turning three francs into
ten sorely tempted Kiki; such a windfall would
permit her picnic to materialise. And when
Grospiron frantically snatched the watch from its
guard, and scrawled an IOU with his name and
address on the tariff, and positively danced before
her with extended arms, she said: "Alors, I risk
it! It is understood that you send me ten francs
to-morrow; and I will post the watch to that

address. Take down mine. I have not a card—give me something to write on.''

He thrust the Alcazar programme on her, stuffed it back in his coat, and, grabbing the loan, rushed out. By a dispensation of Providence, a vacant taxi was at the kerb. He fell into it, half blind with terror. His heart and head were throbbing deafeningly, and as he pelted up the station steps he was voiceless. But a breakneck race along the platform enabled him to catch the train. Half-way to Ville-Nogent, by force of habit, he searched his pockets, to be sure that they contained nothing to incriminate him. Only as he tossed the Alcazar programme through the window did his disordered brain realise that it bore his creditor's address.

He had never read the address. He couldn't send her the ten francs—and she knew where he lived! When she wrote to revile him, his wife might read the letter! He cursed the Joyous Jackdaw, and Paris, and himself. Though he was streaming with perspiration, his teeth chattered like castanets.

For the next few days he felt as if he lived on a bomb.

But Kiki did not write to revile him; her gift for correspondence was by no means equal to what she wanted to say. When five days had passed without the arrival of a remittance, and she had ascertained that the utmost to be realised on the security with a broken mainspring was one franc fifty, she jabbed pins through her hat with an air that boded ill for him, and proceeded "par tram-vay" to make investigations. By tram the journey to Ville-Nogent is slow, but cheap.

The rural aspect of the place appealed to her. And, though she hadn't been sanguine of it, the street existed—and the number was to be discovered too; and a black-and-gold plaque on the white wall announced the domicile to be a boarding-house. The only remaining question in her mind, as she rang the bell, was whether anybody called "Grospiron" boarded there.

The door was opened by a vast woman with a crimson face. The ingratiating smile that she put on made it immediately evident that she was the proprietress.

"Monsieur Grospiron," asked Kiki sweetly— "is he at home?"

The woman, ceasing to try to look like a benign mother, regarded the attractive stranger suspiciously. "No," she grunted. "You see madame Grospiron; what is it that you desire?"

"Tiens!" reflected Kiki delighted; "my little swindler is the boss. And married to a mountain with a temper! This is luck. If he would not rather pay up than be given away I am no judge of red faces." It being necessary to account for her inquiry, she simpered, "Pardon, madame, it is the same thing! I seek a private hotel, and I was told that by far the best was that of monsieur Grospiron."

"Ah!" exclaimed the huge woman, beaming anew. "It is I who conduct the house, mademoiselle—my husband has his business outside. Will you give yourself the trouble of entering?"

Kiki would have preferred to learn forthwith where his business was situated, but she was afraid of displaying too much interest. She promised herself to acquire the information within.

"Here is the dining-room," said madame Grospiron. "It gives on to the beautiful garden. One might be in the heart of the country, n'est ce pas? Everybody finds it a veritable paradise; I have people who return to me again and again. There is a family—very distinguished; the monsieur is an advocate—who have passed every summer with me for twenty years. This year, for the first time, they did not come—they went to Switzerland. They write me, 'We have made an error. Never again! For the future, every summer with you!' The nourishment, how abundant you will find it! And of the first quality I assure you. The menus for this evening are not ready yet, but you will see on the slate in the kitchen what we shall have. A lady and her daughter here—very highly born; they have been accustomed to all that there is the most luxurious—tell me every day, 'There is no place but yours, in all the suburbs of Paris, where we can eat.' How ridiculous they are, the others! What is the use of the fine air for the lungs if there is not good food for the stomach? This way, mademoiselle, if you will be amiable enough to view the bedrooms!''

Kiki was not eager to view the bedrooms; she was no longer impatient even to view her debtor. An inspiration had flashed upon her, and her nimble mind was enchanted by a prospect of blackmail. How far more substantial, how far more chic than the cheap hamper of her dreams would be that abundant nourishment in the dining-room giving on to the beautiful garden! When the bill was presented, the errant husband himself should privately provide the money to pay it.

''I have not explained myself, madame,'' she said. ''I do not come to Ville-Nogent to stay, at present; I desire simply a day's repasts. I propose to spend Sunday here, en plein air, with a little family party. It will be my birthday. If one could arrange for an ample déjeuner, and a good dinner in the tranquil atmosphere of some establishment like this, it appears to me that it would be preferable to taking our meals amid the noise of a café.''

''But assuredly!'' assented the other, crestfallen. ''Then, if you and your friends should be disinclined to make an immediate return to the Park—after a meal one wishes to repose un peu, n'est ce pas?—you will have a garden in the meanwhile. It is much more practical. How many persons? Regard, I can put you at the smaller table all by yourselves!''

''There will be four of us. As to terms? Our

tastes are not extravagant, but if you provide anything special for us, naturally you will increase the price a shade. I shall not complain of that.''

"Listen," said madame Grospiron; "you will be thoroughly content. I shall give you assorted hors d'œuvres—anchovies and butter, salad of tomatoes; then, œufs-sur le-plat, or a rabbit in white wine. . . . That pleases you?''

"I have a fancy for vol-au-vent; let us have a vol-au-vent as well!''

"Certainly!—a nice vol-au-vent. And then, a bifteck cotelette, or a faux filet——''

"A vrai filet!" said Kiki. "The difference in the quality is worth the extra cost.''

"I am of your opinion, mademoiselle! Bien! un vrai filet with fried potatoes. Afterwards, épinards au beurre, compote of apples—it will be the best in your life, because I introduce always a suspicion of vanilla, I!—a sound bordeaux and a cup of coffee that you will pronounce 'superb.' For dinner—But wait! Leave me to arrange, and you will not call it expensive. Ordinarily our charge to a passant is three francs for a luncheon, and four for a dinner. It is not dear, hein? For you I shall make a few improvements, and, as you say, it will come to a trifle more. But with us there are no exorbitant figures. And it will be, I assure you, a veritable menu for a fête—far better than you could procure at a restaurant at double the price! If you will consent to view the bedrooms for later in the season, mademoiselle, there are only a few stairs to mount.''

Kiki returned to Paris enraptured, and called on Tricotrin.

''Ah, mon enfant!'' said the poet, raising his head from his manuscript. ''How goes it? You find me immersed in work.''

''Are you writing a tragedy, Maître?'' asked Kiki with reverence.

''No, but it is a tragedy that I should be writing it; I pronounce a decree, for my Fashions for Men article, on the correct use of the waistcoat slip— an embellishment that I have never possessed the means to adopt. One must live, Kiki, and my Muse is hard of heart.''

''I do not understand what the creature can be thinking of!'' avowed Kiki shyly.

The poet ignored the hint, being at this period faithful to a memory. He did no more than reflect, ''She is charming, this little one!'' and then valiantly reverted to his ordinance on waistcoat slips.

''I have come,'' she continued, subduing a sigh, ''to request the honour of your company to-morrow, and that of your friend, monsieur Pitou. I give a little feast at Ville-Nogent; there will be a déjeuner and a dinner, and my guests are to be stuck for nothing beyond their tram fares.''

''A déjeuner and a dinner?'' cried Tricotrin. ''Are you delirious? How do you do these things? You are bien gentille, Kiki, but while my mouth waters, it is my duty to dissuade you from such regal hospitality."

"You need not consider my outlay—it will be well within my resources!" declared Kiki. And Pitou arriving at this juncture, she went on, "Monsieur Pitou, may I have the pleasure of seeing you lunch and dine with me at Ville-Nogent to-morrow? We are all going to weave daisy-chains and listen to the nightingale, if these things happen to be in season, and put away square meals in the entr'actes."

"She has inherited a million or two, it seems," commented Tricotrin. "What do you say?"

"Of whom does the party consist?" inquired the composer, beginning to tremble.

"There will be," she murmured reflectively, "you, and monsieur Tricotrin, and—I have not asked any one else yet."

"Listen, Kiki!" exclaimed Pitou. "You have a kind nature, but between Louison-Flore and me all is over! She deceived me heartlessly, and I can never pardon her. Do not imagine that by throwing us together for a day you can heal a breach that is eternal." And he folded his arms like the hero of a drama.

"But why tell me what I already know?" remonstrated the girl. "Besides, Louison-Flore would refuse to come if she knew you were to be present. Does she not swear that you misjudged her? Do not fear. Rather than betray to you the tenderness that she still cherishes, the poor child will pine proudly into her grave.''

"As to that," said Pitou, in an emotional voice, "it would, of course, be possible to include her without mentioning my name. Far be it from me to deny you the pleasure of entertaining your own chums!''

Kiki betook herself to Louison-Flore briskly. ''Will you spend a happy day in the country with me to-morrow?''

"Who else is going?" demanded Louison-Flore. "Listen, old dear. I know how well you mean, but Nicolas Pitou and I are strangers to each other ever more! He wronged me cruelly, and I can never forgive him. Do not figure yourself that by popping us together under the same tree you can revive a passion that is extinct.'' And she clenched her hands like the leading lady at the Ambigu.

"But why inform me of what I have heard a thousand times?" expostulated Kiki. "Besides, monsieur Pitou would decline my invitation if he guessed you were to be there. Does he not realise that you are adamant to his sufferings? Have no misgiving. Rather than let you see the despair that is devouring him, the poor lad will waste away into his tomb.''

"So far as that goes," said Louison-Flore chokily, "if you are keen on asking him, there is nothing to prevent your doing so without alluding to me. I am the last person to expect my personal

sorrows to forbid you the society of your own
friends.''

''Tiens!'' thought Kiki, ''these two are going
to be all right. If only the poet would look more
favourably on little me!''

''You got your ten francs then, after all?''
said Louison-Flore.

''No,'' said Kiki; ''but, between ourselves, the
crook is a married man, and runs a pension de
famille. It is there that we feed to-morrow. I
project it as a joyful surprise to him!''

''But it will come very dear, that?'' ejaculated
the other, after a stare, bursting into laughter.

''On the contrary! If he does not wish me to
refer my claim to his wife, it will come very cheap.
Not a word to the boys about it, mind!''

With what dignity next morning did Pitou and
Louison-Flore dissemble the shock that they felt
at seeing each other! With what tact was her
tram-fare paid by Tricotrin, while Kiki's fare was
defrayed by Pitou! And how Arcadian were the
tortuous paths that repeatedly separated the ex-
cursionists into couples! The luncheon hour arrived too soon for everybody.

What shall be said, however, of the guests' enthusiasm when they were conducted to that
luncheon? The young men could scarcely unfold
their napkins for bewilderment, and Louison-Flore
kicked her hostess in ecstasy under the table.
''She transports us to scenes of splendour!''
gasped the poet. ''It is a chapter out of *The*

Thousand-And-One Nights! Am I daft, or is that item on the menu vol-au-vent?''

It was when they had begun to fall to on the anchovies and butter, with fascinated glances towards the boarders, who, in various stages of decrepitude, shuffled in on sticks, that the unsuspecting Grospiron appeared. To Grospiron's haunting fear of an abusive letter reaching the wrong hands, the Sabbath was promising a brief respite, for there was no more than one postal delivery on Sunday, and that was over. He entered with his first appetite since the hard-boiled eggs. As the thunderbolt of Kiki's countenance smote his sight in the very heart of his pension de famille the man jerked so electrically that, if his wife had not had her face in her soup-plate, nothing could have saved him.

He crumpled into his chair with his faculties spinning. From the sick void where his stomach had been, tremors rose clammily to the crown of his head. By a desperate effort he effected a signal of secret understanding, but it was received with a glare of scorn. What did her presence portend? How to obtain a clandestine word with her? He dared not refuse his food, lest he arouse his better half to watchfulness, and the protests of his œsophagus under the compulsion that he put upon it to swallow, were something frightful. When the deaf boarder opposite condemned him to the torture of bawling small talk, death would have come as a happy release.

Not till the evening, after the bohemians had returned to a recherché dinner, bearing great bunches of wild flowers, had he a chance of the clandestine word. Then his creditor sought him.

"Many thanks for a delightful day, monsieur," she said. "Your wife's bill comes to fifty-six francs seventy-five!" And she held out a cheeky palm.

"*Comment?* What do you say?" stuttered the wretched man. "Listen, ma petite, you are doing me a grave injustice! I am honest; I am enchanted by this opportunity to hand you the ten-franc piece and regain my property. I swear it to you! When we parted, I intended most conscientiously to remit, but in my excitement I threw your address out of the train."

"Bien sûr!" said the girl. "It was the same with me; when I started I intended most conscientiously to pay, but in my excitement I threw out my purse. . . . Fifty-six francs seventy-five! Do not put me to any inconvenience in collecting it, or we will all come and stay for a month."

"Are you mad?" shrieked Grospiron. "You commit an outrage. Have you no conscience? Fifty-six francs seventy-five, in addition to what I squandered in Paris? And for what? I cannot do it! Do you imagine I have such a sum lying loose in my pocket? C'est énorme. Show me the bill. Fifty-six francs seventy-five for two meals? It is robbery!"

"Well, let it be a lesson to you not to overcharge

here for the future!" said Kiki. "Your wife ex-
pects me in her office in half an hour; would you
prefer to supply me with the sum in the meanwhile, or for me to show her your IOU and your
watch?"

Some little time afterwards, when the watch
was back in Grospiron's keeping, and the receipted
bill was in the young lady's sac-à-main, Tricotrin
murmured to Pitou:

"What a revelation she has been, that girl!
Her mind is a fountain of allurements. To me
this festival has yielded the most delicious of dis-
coveries!"

"To me, also," responded the composer raptly.
"For I have learnt that Louison-Flore was faithful to me always—and she has pardoned my abominable suspicion."

Stars winked over the Land of Cockaigne as the
two pairs of Parisians wound their way to the
station.

"There is but one crumpled rose-leaf in my
Eden," breathed the poet, an arm round his hostess's waist. "Thou wert in no position to afford
the lavish entertainment thou hast showered on
us."

"Ah, tais-toi!" cooed Kiki. "The avowal of
thy tenderness awakes in me emotions so unforeseen that—without exaggeration—I cannot remember that the day cost me anything except my
heart!"

VIII

The Poet Grows Practical

IF you were on the boulevard de Rochechouart, not far from the rue des Martyrs, that New Year's Day about 4.15 p. m., you may have seen a little lady, who was returning from a rehearsal, exchange a careless bow with two young gentlemen who were removing their household belongings in a hip bath. This is the history of that bow.

It is communicated, under the veil of fictitious names—the surname of "de Varangeville" is manifestly feigned—lest any student of the present volume should be in danger of assuming that the poet's only qualification for literary eminence was his long hair.

One night he remarked abruptly, "There are people who regard me as a dreamer, a poet without a practical side to him!"

Pitou responded, "There is a poor composer who knows you thoroughly."

"Nevertheless I am about to say something that will astonish you. Some months ago I stumbled upon a little café in the rue des Batignolles where a Martell, three stars, cost only ten sous——"

"Astonishing, in truth! You mentioned it at the time."

"That is not the point of my narrative. This afternoon while I was debating which should be the first theatre to refuse my new comedy—I have decided to entitle it *La Feuillaison*—my constitution demanded such refreshment. The little café recurred to me fondly. It was a long way to go, but I remembered that the glass at ten sous had been of more generous dimensions than one gets at places where the price is twelve, and fifteen—to say nothing of haunts of fashion where they have the impudence to charge thirty. Well, when I arrived in the street, what was my chagrin to find myself uncertain which of the cafés it was——"

"I am astonished, as you foresaw," put in Pitou.

"Peste! the point is still ahead. You shall have a cue for that astonishment of yours. I took a seat on a bench, searching my memory. Beside me a bill-sticker was posting playbills on a colonne Morris. One of them announced the forthcoming piece by de Varangeville—his third this year—and I smiled to note with what miraculous speed some of our popular dramatists can supply a laboriously constructed play. A hen does not lay an egg so casually."

"The toil is divided," said the composer; "an obscure man writes the play, and the popular man writes his name."

"Don't be trite. To-day I fell to studying the

obscure man's philosophy, and I found something
to be said for it by a poor devil who trudges kilo-
mètres to save a copper. It is true that he has no
laurels, but he has dinners; the back that he turns
upon ambition has a good coat on it. Though he
does not earn any kudos, he earns a living. Nicolas,
as I sat there, opposite the Mairie in the rue des
Batignolles, staring at the colonne Morris, it was
revealed to me why I am perennially hard up;
I saw why I have struggled and achieved nothing
—why our attic is a cemetery of rejected plays.
They have been submitted in the wrong quarters;
I have sent them to theatrical managers—I should
have offered them to popular playwrights.''

Pitou stood horrified.

''Well, it is not too late to turn my meditations
to account! I cannot propose to celebrities that
they should father manuscripts that have been
hawked round Paris bearing my own autograph—
nor, as a matter of fact, are they all quite so tran-
scendent as I once thought them—but *La Feuillaison* is virgin. I have determined to sacrifice
it upon the altar of Mammon.''

''I forbid thee to talk so!'' cried Pitou. ''Yes,
my astonishment is immense, and I condemn the
cue with all my heart. You, whose unfaltering
aspiration and resolve has helped me to bear my
own adversities, you talk of bartering your heri-
tage for the wages of a 'ghost'? What would the
dinners and the coat amount to in your apostasy?
Thistles, and a horsehair shirt! Better a herring,

and no socks, with the prospect of renown! My
friend, your reflections on the bench were rotten.
Remember that the virgin is not too literary to be
amusing, and shut up.''

''My more than brother, how rejoiced I am to
find that you agree with me!'' returned Tricotrin
affectionately.

''What do you say?''

''My sacrifice will not extend to the lengths
that you assume. My first thought, I avow, was
to permit another chap to appropriate all the
credit for what I have done; but the notion was
commonplace—I felt it to be unworthy of me. I
sat seeking a more brilliant scheme, a sacrifice
with inspiration. Bref, I have decided to retain
half the credit, and half the fees; I shall read my
completed play to de Varangeville and suggest
that he figures as part author of it.''

''*That* I approve!'' ejaculated Pitou, admir-
ingly. ''You will be parting with a good deal,
but—ma foi! if de Varangeville consents to an
ostensible collaboration, it will be an enormous
thing. The piece might be done at the Gymnase;
you will become a playwright of the Boulevard;
you will never look back!''

''That's it!''

''You have a head on you!''

''Yes, my practical side is to be top dog henceforward. Artistically, of course, it is atrocious,
heartrending, and diabolical that I cannot do without him—and I shall need all your sympathy to

sustain me; indeed, I do not know in which case I
shall be the more trying—if the play succeeds and
he gets half the admiration, or if it fails and there
isn't any. 'Zere's ze rub,' as 'Amlet says! But
commercially, the project is sound. It promises
a fat purse. Conspuez ideals, larks, love affairs!
I am a new man with an eye to the main chance."

How little the belauded and prosperous de
Varangeville, in his majestic study, divined that,
in a distant garret, two shabby bohemians had
settled for him the terms of a secret partnership!

And the initial difficulty was how to enlighten
him. The tactful request for an interview "on
a matter of mutual interest," which had been in-
dited as soon as his address was ascertained from
Bottin, evoked no answer.

"He deserves that I should let him slide!"
said the poet wrathfully. "If it were not that
my judgment tells me he is the man for my purpose, I would promptly transfer the opportunity
to somebody else. Now what am I to do—I cannot persuade myself that my eloquence is likely
to accomplish much if I waylay him in the street?
Yet another of those problems that punctuate our
chequered careers confronts us! Query: how to
obtain an appointment with a personage who
ignores one's letters?"

"We could not beat up any one who might
manage to procure a line of introduction for
you?" said Pitou dubiously.

"You are right," said Tricotrin; "we couldn't."
The young men pondered.

"To-morrow," said Pitou, "is to see the répéti-
tion générale of his new thing. There should be
a hint derivable from that. But I confess that I
fail to grasp it."

Tricotrin raised his head:

"We are on the right track, though. Yes.
Wait! I approach an idea. . . . Which journal
shall I choose? I think *Le Demi-Mot*. Upon my
word, I believe I see my way!"

And next morning he called upon the Editor
of *Le Demi-Mot*.

"Monsieur," he announced, "I am about to
spend an afternoon with my friend de Varangeville, and I shall be in a position to supply copy of
a far more intimate nature than the ordinary in-
terviewer can hope to get hold of. Would it suit
your policy to take a thousand words from me at
a special rate?"

The Editor, who was wide-awake, too, did not
commit himself; but the visit enabled the applicant to annex a sheet of note-paper headed *Le
Demi-Mot* in imposing type. And equipped with
this, he wrote to de Varangeville again. The epistle was actually penned, in the attic, before the
gentleman's piece had seen the light, but it was
not dispatched till afterwards, of course. It ran
thus:

"Monsieur—What a work of genius is your
play! With what spirituality, what wit and in-

sight you have conducted this exquisite comedy in
which life is viewed always through the medium
of your delicate and poetical imagination—in
which tears of sensibility are always near to joyous smiles! How enchanting it is, how ravishing,
how irresistible! Dare I hope that you will favour
us with your views upon the interpretation of
your chef d'œuvre for the purpose of a special article? I should be honoured to call upon you at
any hour.

"Receive, monsieur, I pray you, the expression
of my sentiments the most distinguished—Gustave
Tricotrin."

To the appreciative Pitou, the correspondent
observed, "If he does not jump at the chance of
doing the box office a bit of good I am a babe in
arms. I collar two birds with one stone, voyons,
for it will be as easy as shelling peas to dish up
a column or so for *Le Demi-Mot* out of our little
chat. This calls for drinks; à cheval!"

Paris was mauve, and the glare of electricity
had begun to leap into the waning daylight when
the poet descended the rue Lepic and proceeded
anxiously towards the more opulent district in
which de Varangeville dwelt. What a crisis had
arrived! If the scheme came off, the humble
scribe, to whom a louis looked as big as a cart-
wheel, might be a distinguished author in a fur
overcoat by Christmas. His brain span in thinking of it; and as he passed through the porte

cochère, and went up the carpeted staircase, he
wiped beads of trepidation from his brow.

De Varangeville had paid him the compliment
of setting a scene for him. The successful dramatist was discovered in the flood of composition,
and a richly embroidered dressing-gown. En-
treating monsieur Tricotrin's patience for a few
minutes, he strode about the room, alternately
clapping a hand to his heart, and apostrophising
the heavens, while he dictated a torrent of emotional dialogue to his stenographer. The rapidity
with which polished speeches poured from his
mouth would have been miraculous if they had not
been written already and committed to memory
for the purpose of impressing the newspaper-man.

"Ça y est!" he panted, falling into a chair.
"A thousand apologies, monsieur; I must beseech
your pardon! That situation rushed upon me
an instant since, and the artist in me would not
be denied. I am enchanted to have the opportunity to—— Ah! a moment more, I pray you.
Mademoiselle: a correction for the penultimate
line; for 'without thee my heaven would be a
blank,' substitute 'without thee my heaven would
be a void.' C'est tout, you may retire. Voilà,
monsieur! I am wholly at your service, though
I confess to the fear that I have but little to say.
The sensational triumph that we have just
achieved—the box office is veritably besieged!—
is the result of a nerve strain positively terrible.
Never before in my career have I rehearsed so

strenuously, never have I hurled the stimulus of
my personality into a production with such boundless force. I am suffering from the reaction; I
should have a tranquil environment, I should have
absolute repose: but que voulez-vous? The overwhelming pressure of other work cannot be es-
caped—and one must avow the truth!—I would
not escape it if I could. A-ah! there is the secret.
My bondage is sweet to me. I shall die in harness,
but my shafts are decked with flowers. Mon
Dieu, how inexorable, but how alluring is this
art!''

''You cannot act so well as you can write!''
reflected Tricotrin. ''If I had not more valuable
fish to fry, I could do a column on you that would
tickle Paris to death.'' And aloud he murmured,
''The Muses like their joke, monsieur—to be a
Master one must be a slave.'' But both his responses and his questions were superfluous—de
Varangeville had decided what he was going to
say, and said it.

It was when his performance had concluded and
he looked for Tricotrin to get up, that the visitor began nervously to shuffle his feet. At last,
with a slight stammer, he said:

''It has been a great joy to me to be received
by you, monsieur. May I own that I had personal
reasons for aspiring to the privilege? I am not
journalist solely; I am dramatist as well.''

''Tiens!'' said de Varangeville, who was not in
the least interested to hear it.

"I even venture to think that you would see merit in my latest comedy. How hard it is for a writer without reputation to gain an entrance! Actually I delay to offer my piece now that it is written."

"One must persevere," yawned the other; "one must continue always."

"A piece that strikes a totally new note—a note that will startle. With a small cast—no long salary list for a manager to pay—no elaborate mise en scène for him to shy at And with qualities that render it a lucrative property for America and England." (He added mentally, "That ought to fetch you!") "Oh," he exclaimed, "there is money in it, pots of money! Yet because I am unknown it can go begging."

"You have not yet submitted it anywhere?" inquired de Varangeville.

"Nowhere. For one thing, the ink on it has not long been dry; and for another, when your amiable note arrived, the daring fancy seized me that, if I should catch you in a generous mood, you might deign to hear it and grant me a little guidance."

"Ah, par exemple!" cried the dramatist wildly, "have you any conception, my young friend, of the demands upon my time?"

"What a boon, what a priceless service it would be!" urged Tricotrin, taking the manuscript from beneath his pèlerine. "By a single suggestion you might double the value of my play. *My* play?

It would suddenly be yours too! Audacious as it sounds, I should be uplifted to the plane of a collaborator. Ah, consider, monsieur! I realise that I appear to you a novice, I realise that you believe this work to be waste-paper—I realise that you would perhaps be justified in wagering a hundred to one that it is waste-paper; yet you will not deny that there exists the remote contingency that it isn't? Well, have a gamble, listen to the first Act! True, it will cost you forty precious minutes, but risk forty minutes for the chance of gaining a six months' run!"

"You are a droll chap," laughed de Varangeville, attracted in spite of himself. "Well, fire away, then! But I warn you that if I find you have been talking through your hat, I shall ring the curtain down long before the Act is done."

"What a chapter for my Biography!" thought the poet, trembling in every nerve.

The celebrity's thoughts were (1) "I am an ass to consent"; (2) "There may be something in it, after all"; (3) "Sapristi! I am going to hear this right through!" And when the crowning words of the final Act had been uttered—when the author, with his heart full of excitement, and his head full of his beautiful lines, prayed breathlessly for an emotional tribute from the Master—the Master mused, "All the alteration that it needs I could make in a day. No work to do, and the lion share of the fees would not be half bad business!"

Some forty minutes later Tricotrin, whose capital was five francs, reeled into an auto-taxi, and spread his limbs in it as extensively as he could. "Hoot!" he commanded, as his slum was reached. "Continuous and triumphant hoots!" The magnificence of the arrival brought Pitou tumbling out upon the pavement, white-faced. "This sovereign splendour can mean only that you have conquered?" he gasped. And, falling into his arms, the poet babbled incoherently.

"C'est épatant!" cried the musician again and again when details were unfolded. "Mon Dieu, it is like a fairy tale, it is the summit—you have arrived! And what house—did he say what house was probable?"

"The Vaudeville! They have been pestering him to give them something. 'By André de Varangeville and Gustave Tricotrin!' Though it is an outrage that his name should come first, that won't look so dusty on the bills of the Vaudeville —hein? I shall buy a camp stool and sit outside the theatre all day admiring them. Well, I could not arrange for an equal division of royalties; instead of 50 per cent., I have agreed to accept 40. After all, it is good enough—he gets 10 per cent. more than I do."

"He gets 20 per cent. more than you do," said Pitou.

"What? How do you make that out? I should have had fifty, and I have consented to forty; so I cede him 10 per cent."

"But his share is 20 per cent. more than yours."

"How can ten be twenty, duffer?"

"You do not follow me!"

"Morbleu! he cannot receive twenty, since I only give him ten."

"No, listen! You are to have forty?"

"Yes."

"Forty from a hundred leaves sixty?"

"It does," assented Tricotrin, after consideration.

"Which goes to de Varangeville?"

"Right!"

"Enfin, if he gets sixty while you get forty, he gets 20 per cent. more than you."

"It is black magic!" faltered the poet, dismayed. "It appears that he is a sharper. I agreed to ten, and it becomes twenty! It is a great deal, that; it is far too much. Do you think the vagaries of arithmetic are liable to make it more still presently? You know, you have the brain of a financier! I also am a business man, but I see largely—I am not altogether infallible in the minutiæ of affairs." And his exultation was damped for a quarter of an hour, as he dwelt upon de Varangeville's share.

However, there was a brighter prospect to dwell on. Probably no greater sensation had ever been known in the Café du Bel Avenir than he created, during the one-franc dinner, when he remarked listlessly, "Ah, by the way, de Varangeville and I have decided to do a piece together!" So stupe-

fied was Lajeunie that he put a mussel into his
mouth shell and all, and the waiter, who over-
heard the announcement, ran, round-eyed, to report it to the proprietress. She could not fail to
be impressed, though her comment was the French
for "Rats!"

Indeed, there were moments when the poet himself came near to wondering whether it wasn't
"rats"—whether the brilliant outlook that daz-
zled him was not destined to conclude with that
familiar curtain, "And then he woke up!" Divers
as were the moods in which he had promenaded
the boulevard de Rochechouart during his siege
of Paris, never before had he paced it in such a
one as this. When he stalked, with a pass, now
into the fauteuils of some minor theatre, he foresaw himself conspicuous in a loge and evening
dress at the Vaudeville. When he cooked herrings and lentils for his evening repast in the
attic, he anticipated ecstatically the cuisine of
Paillard's.

And need one say that Pitou was to participate
in the splendours—Lajeunie, and Sanquereau, and
Didier as well, for that matter, but Pitou before
all? Pitou's compositions were no longer to lack
a friend at court to call attention to their excellence; within twelve months, at the outside, the
music of Nicolas Pitou was to be the rage! It
was all decided.

A month passed; and though de Varangeville
had not found time to consider further the altera-

tions that he had vaguely contemplated, it was
elysian to be received by him and mark his infinite
confidence. To offer a comedy, and to place it
appeared to be, with him, one and the same thing.
True, the nectar was adulterated; he seemed unconscious that as yet he had not contributed a
single idea to the piece and had a maddening trick
of referring to some of its best features as suggestions of his own. But, his boasts being blent with
compliments, it would have been unbecoming to
cavil. He would say, in a most gracious way:

"Your journalism has distinction, you know;
that article in *Le Demi-Mot* was capitally done.
For that matter, you are not altogether without
the sense of the theatre—I see some dramatic
promise in you. To others it would not be per-
ceptible, but I see it, myself. I detect in your
stuff a ray that makes me hopeful of you. One
day you will write a play. Do not despair. You
will learn. You are quick to seize the value of a
hint, my young friend—it is not many young men
of your age who would have grasped so promptly
the reasons why their piece was no good."

A little later on he was referring to all its best
features as suggestions of his own; and unmindful
of the "quickness to seize the value of a hint,"
deplored pathetically that every one of the suggestions had been opposed.

"What an undertaking it was to convince you
that these improvements were necessary!" he
mourned. "What endless arguments! They wore

me out. The trouble with you young men is that
you regard every line you write as sacred—it must
not be touched! You resent the deletion of a syllable. But is it not always frightful to me to
collaborate? Veritably, it is a curse. A thousand
times I have sworn never to collaborate again. To
write a great play alone consumes my energies
far less—it makes less demand on my invention,
is in every respect less exhausting—than to work
on some little thing with a collaborator."

And Tricotrin ached to answer, "In our case,
however, you haven't tried working yet!" But
he was heroically dumb. Only to Pitou did he
let himself go. "Oh, mon Dieu!" wailed the
aspiring playwright, "what one has to put up
with, in being practical."

When he had at last perused the piece, pencil
in hand, de Varangeville decided that three of
the scenes must be wholly reconstructed. And one
morning he actually sat down to reconstruct them.
But, on second thoughts, he sent for his collaborator to do it, instead. So Tricotrin sweated in his
attic for a fortnight, and then read the new scenes
to the great man, who reclined on a yellow sofa,
smoking a cigar. And when the reading was concluded, de Varangeville wiped beads from his brow
and said faintly, "Thank God, the toil of creation is now over! I could have done no more."

During the evening he rallied sufficiently to
write a six-page letter specifying his symptoms in
"this reaction, when I must face the sombre truth

that I am on the verge of mental and physical collapse."

Tricotrin, as in duty bound, paid a visit of sympathy, and found him disposing of a Gargantuan repast.

"I am more dead than alive," repined the glutton. "It is always so when I have completed a play—above all, after the strain of collaborating. I see that some paper questions which of the social evils is the worst; I could supply the answer: collaboration! Do not distress yourself; I have only my own literary excesses to thank. While I am at work I do not notice how prodigally I am pouring it out; or, if my nerves expostulate, the tornado of my imagination refuses to be checked. So long as there is work to be done, I am a giant squandering his forces; and then—what will you? —I am like this!" He feebly shook his head, and attacked the fourth course—a fillet and fried potatoes.

"Literally, I swoon in thinking of the weight I must support when the piece goes into rehearsal," he resumed, grabbing the mustard. "I ask myself, trembling, 'How will you survive it?' *Your* little part of the work is done, fortunate young man, but for *me* remains the achievement that will quadruple the value of the play. Stupendous! You do not dream what you will owe to my labours at rehearsal; you do not dream what inversions and transmutations I make in a play when I begin to build it up before me on the stage. Astounding! I live in the theatre; if I withdraw for a moment it is fatal. I never eat. I never sleep. Of course it is suicide,"—he smacked his lips over another glass of burgundy, and assumed a posture of dauntless command—"but I know that I must keep my hand at the helm. For instance, they say to me, 'What a fine scene you have given us here—how splendidly it will go!' I reply, 'It is atrocious—it disgusts me.' They are dumbfounded. 'Do not speak to me,' I tell them—'I must find some idea.' The company regard me, breathless. I close my eyes. Like this. Suddenly I utter the inspired decree: 'We shall turn that scene upside down!' As a result, the play takes Paris by storm. Mon Dieu! you have got a soft partnership; by rights I ought to charge you ten thousand francs for what I shall have to do to the piece at rehearsal!"

However, he contented himself with sending a typewritten copy at which Tricotrin looked distractedly for his own name. Sobbing with wrath, he saw, beautifully spaced:

LA FEUILLAISON

COMEDY IN FOUR ACTS

BY

ANDRÉ DE VARANGEVILLE.

He arrived at the majestic study head first. "*Comment donc?* I have had nothing at all to do with the play, then, hein? My name is invisible!" he gasped.

"Is it so?" asked de Varangeville, gently surprised; "I had not remarked the detail. What do these things matter?"

"Matter? Whether I remain unknown, or not? It is of some slight consequence. To me, anyhow! That is why I sign my work. And I am not unique. Other authors have the same idiosyncrasy. I believe it is rather usual to find an author's name on a play? What do you imagine I write for? Money? As well! Not solely. If money were all I wanted, I should not write at all. I could do better in business. Matter? Before I would consent to remove my name from the play I would tear the four acts into pipe-spills!"

"But compose yourself, my young friend, I pray you!" expostulated de Varangeville blandly. "The duologue does not call for pipe-spills. If you set any store by it, your name is easily added. I attach no importance to such trifles, myself; I am too old a hand at the game—I am not out for laurels. All that concerns me is to get a success. Whether it bears one name, or two—I am above these vanities! Ah, at your age—I understand! It is natural. I do not reproach you; I can make allowances." And, having flourished a pen, he wrote the name, after his own, with an air of so much toleration and benignity that Tricotrin nearly felt contrite for having complained of the outrage.

Thus the poet's mighty project of collaboration was fulfilled. And then, in the history of the project, an unforeseen event occurred: the Heroine entered.

She entered, in a very dirty white frock, with a bouquet of rag roses in her hand, as the ingénue in a fourth-rate theatre one night; and the young man, who had been yawning dismally, sat up in his chair. His admiration for her histrionic gifts, which were not unusual, may have originated in the fact that she boasted two attributes which were very unusual indeed in an ingénue there— youth and good looks; but he beheld a situation entirely after his own heart. He beheld Gustave Tricotrin, the dramatist, discovering a star! He applauded like one whose approval was a cachet. Ostentatiously he underlined the name of "Mlle. Delacour" on his programme. "She will go far, that little one!" he murmured, loud enough to be heard by his neighbours. Several of them turned to regard him. It was extremely pleasant; he had rarely enjoyed himself in a theatre so much.

Presently it occurred to him that it would be a kindly act to inform her that she had won a dramatist's approval; he perceived that the legitimate sequel to the situation was for him to utter a few encouraging words to the attractive girl. When the representation of the ancient melodrama was complete, therefore, he proceeded with importance to the stage door, and though he did not possess a card, the tone in which he pronounced his name was so impressive that it did the trick. He was admitted to her dressing-room.

The expression of interest observable on mademoiselle Delacour's piquant face, as he entered, faded somewhat as she noted the stranger's shabby cloak. But the next instant she questioned whether he might not be "somebody" after all. Having advanced to the centre of the room, with the gravity of the Directeur of the Théâtre Français, and contemplated her in silence for some seconds, the young man said solemnly:

"Mon enfant, well done! Your performance pleases me—I am content."

"Oh, monsieur!" she faltered.

"Not often can a playwright of the Boulevard commend a performance in shows like this! But I find much that is thoughtful in your work. Continue, my child, continue with confidence. It is I who say it—you will arrive!"

Now, it must not be inferred that no one but Tricotrin thought well of her abilities—happy-go-lucky little bohemian though she was, she had a good opinion of them herself; and at the words "a playwright of the Boulevard" she did not doubt that an offer was on the way.

"Ciel! but you make me proud, monsieur!" she murmured. And, throwing up her eyes, she went on in the difficult key that the gentleman seemed to expect of her: "How I adore it, my beautiful art! What devotion it inspires in me! My dream is, that I may one day interpret a rôle of subtlety.

Ah, quel bonheur! Is it not rapture to study in
that hope—to study, though one knows that a
lifetime itself would be insufficient to master even
half the complexities of an art at once so elusive
and profound?''

"Ah, mais non!'' said Tricotrin to himself; ''I
had to stomach that sort of tosh from de Varangeville, but I am not here to stick it from you!''
He replied: ''Tiens! Well, to descend from the
hilltop, I am very glad to make your acquaintance.
If I may say so, you are even prettier 'off' than
'on.' ''

"Too amiable, monsieur!'' she smiled, not unwilling to be herself again. The glance that she
cast at him was, indeed, liable to be called coquet-
tish. Then in a voice disconcertingly brisk, she
added:

"Having bumped to business, as you suggest,
may I ask why you wished to see me?''

"Er—why I wished to see you?'' said Tricotrin.

"Just so!'' said she. And now there was a
shade of impatience in her voice.

"Well,'' he acknowledged, ''you have put a
very interesting question to me. Why did I wish
to see you? A minute since I believed that I
knew; suddenly I begin to ask myself if my motives were not more intricate than I realised. That
I was moved to congratulate you is perfectly true.
Do not query that. If you have any doubt on the
point, I will congratulate you again. But now
that I find myself in your presence I am not cer-

tain, upon my word, but what the mortal girl influenced me as much as the divine artist. Assuredly your reception of me would fall short of
my ideal if you continued to address me in the
strain of a popular actress being interviewed for
the Press.''

Subduing a smile, she said sharply:

''I say! Are you a dramatist really?''

''If I am a dramatist?'' cried the poet. ''Mon
Dieu! Oh, you will not better that! Posterity
will hold its sides when it reads that question. If
I am a dramatist! Have you ever heard the name
of 'de Varangeville'?''

''What about him?''

''He is a collaborator of mine, that is all. Oh
yes, I am very much a dramatist! Do not figure
yourself, because affectations are foreign to my
nature, that I am of no account. I may not, in
this scene, be precisely famous—I may not be
opulent—but I am a very gifted chap.''

She smiled outright now. ''Well, don't forget
me when your piece is ready to be cast!''

''Have no misgivings! My recognition of your
talents increases with every line you speak. The
rôle of 'Fifi' in my comedy might actually have
been written for you.''

''Comme vous êtes gentil!'' she exclaimed—and
was sorry that the need for exchanging her stage
costume for her own frock forbade her to prolong
the conversation indefinitely.

Tricotrin regretted it no less than she.

"If I might be permitted to wait outside while you make your toilette, I could give you an idea of the part in escorting you home," he suggested. Mademoiselle Delacour yielded a graceful assent. And, though a stroll through the least frequented streets with a captivating companion on his arm was far from being the kind of thing that he had foreseen in the fauteuils, it proved a by no means disagreeable development. At the outset, to be sure, some suspicion of his veracity seemed to linger in her mind; but when his flow of details had persuaded her that she was not being hoaxed, the soft pressure of her arm was almost a caress.

And, in every minute, Tricotrin the sentimental grew more oblivious of the potential star, and more appreciative of the captivating companion. In the life of every bohemian, shiftless, fantastic, or sordid as it may be, there persists one imperishable hope—the hope that circumstances will reveal a confidante who will understand and adore him.

"But 'Fifi' herself?" she asked. "Is it a big part—what does she do?"

"She loves," said Tricotrin.

"And besides?"

"She is unmercenary. An actress naturally mercenary could not play 'Fifi'—she would lack the temperament; 'Fifi' loves a poor man."

"As for me, I thoroughly comprehend that that could occur."

"It promises well for your success. Hard up

though he is, he can render her a valuable service, and this makes him diffident of avowing his tenderness—he would not have her think him one of those odious creatures who say to a girl, 'Yes, I will further your career, but only on conditions!' "

"Ah!" she said.

"But 'Fifi' is shrewd. She perceived the sincerity of his attachment even in their first meeting. They sauntered together at Montmartre under the moon, as you and I are sauntering now, and he confided to her his prospects and ambitions."

"It is pretty!"

"There is reality in it, n'est ce pas? The poor boy's pockets were so light that he was unable to propose supper, and he blushed in wondering what she thought of his omission. But 'Fifi' did not wrong him by supposing that it was because he was mean."

"As if she would!"

"A propos, mademoiselle, I see a café opposite! Will you do me the honour to sip a bock while I tell you the rest?"

"With much pleasure, monsieur."

"The best he could do was to offer her a bock. They seated themselves in a corner of the little terrace, just as you and I have seated ourselves, and——"

"There are in fact several points of resemblance?"

"I do not deny it. But he possessed one dra-

matic advantage that I lack. When he could sup-
press the truth no longer and his homage burst
from him, he knew her christian name.''

Mademoiselle Delacour was not immediately re-
sponsive to this hint.

"Of course, courtships go faster on the stage
than they do off it!" she reminded him.

"Do not disparage my plot; if there is no such
thing as love at first sight, the comedy is a frost!"

"Off it, a girl takes longer to be sure of her
heart.''

"How long?"

"Ah, that depends!"

"On what?"

"For one thing, on the value of the heart.''

"I shall not disguise from you," said Tricotrin
earnestly, "that it is your own heart that I have
in mind. Perhaps you have suspected it?''

Perhaps she had. But what neither of them
suspected yet was that three o'clock was to boom
before they parted from each other regretfully on
her doorstep. How true it is that only the unforeseen comes to pass! At fifteen minutes to midnight they had never met, yet the actress mounted
her black staircase in a highly romantic mood, and
the poet made for his garret, murmuring rhymes
to the name of "Yvette."

"Where on earth have you been all this time?"
growled the composer, whom his entrance wakened.

"The most extraordinary experience!" cried

Tricotrin rapturously. "I have not only discovered the ideal 'Fifi' for *La Feuillaison,* but I have
found the one woman in the world who has ever
fully comprehended me!"

"Again?"

"Ah, this is no illusion, I assure you. I am a
changed man! She is adorable. What sensibility! Figure yourself that we took a bock together
after the performance, and that ever since we
have been walking up and down the avenue de St.
Ouen—which had become a glen in Arcadia—
talking of the future!"

"You are a changed man, with original ideas
of a pleasant evening," was the composer's comment. And he fell asleep again, little surmising
to what the avenue de St. Ouen was to lead.

It was not the last night on which that normally
unattractive thoroughfare revealed Arcadian
qualities to the poet and the actress; nor was it
long before she consented to receive him at more
conventional hours in her lodging. He had announced his dramatic "find" to de Varangeville,
post-haste, on eight enthusiastic pages, and
though de Varangeville had not written yet to express his joy, Yvette was studying the rôle of
"Fifi" daily. Tricotrin conducted the rehearsals
of it with all the assiduity that his devotion would
allow, but interludes were frequent. As the grand
passion was now mutual, it was no rare event for
a rehearsal to begin at midday and conclude only

when the time came for her to remember that she was an ingénue.

"How insufferable," she would lament, "to descend to that rotten part after thy chef d'œuvre, Gustave!"

And Tricotrin would reply, "Courage, my angel; it is for the moment only! Wilt thou not soon be 'Fifi' at the Vaudeville?"

It was with a joyous project, and an elastic step that he sallied forth one morning some three weeks later. He had now pronounced her "exquisite" as "Fifi"; and even Pitou, to whom her type of beauty did not appeal, had conceded grudgingly that she "might have been worse." The poet foresaw a triumphant afternoon. He intended nothing less than to obtain an appointment for her to startle his "collaborator" with her genius.

"How goes it?" inquired de Varangeville. "I have not forgotten you; a dozen times I have had the intention of scribbling a line, but . . . you understand?"

"Ah, I know well!" said the poet, dropping into the velvet armchair on the hearth. "No news?"

"What will you? While the business keeps up there with the thing that they are playing, they will have no ears for anything else. As soon as it begins to drop, our comedy will be in their hands. Do not fear!"

"Ah, it was not that I was impatient, no, no!" said Tricotrin. "My motive in coming was to ask you to grant me a pleasure; and in truth, to

accept a pleasure in return. If you can spare an
hour this afternoon it is my intention to give you
a treat.''

"Ah! What is that?''

"Well, I desire you to hear an actress who pos-
sesses gifts of an order which I venture to assert
you will find amazing.''

"Ah, yes, I remember! The little girl at the
Moncey, or the Montmartre, or the—what was
it? Well, you know, mon vieux, it was absurd,
that! It was an access of imbecility.''

"Imbecility?'' ejaculated Tricotrin. "I do not
follow you!''

"You are not seriously expecting me to entrust
a part of prominence to a woman absolutely unknown? Merci! She is, if you please, a histrionic diamond mine. But it is for somebody else to
erect the machinery! It is not I who am ambitious of these distinctions.''

"*Mais—— Comment?* . . . There is nobody
else who can realise the character so perfectly!''
gasped her lover. "I assure you!''

"Perhaps; I will not dispute it. I should be
a hypocrite to pretend that I am convinced, but
it is not necessary that we argue the point. Her
talents are irrelevant. I have one unswerving rule
—I engage the artists whom the public flock to
see. Give me a Blondette, who cannot act and
cannot sing, but who is a beautiful woman and
draws all Paris, in preference to a genius whose
popularity has still to be achieved!''

"But—it does not hold water, that! If everybody proceeded on the same lines, it is obvious that no actor or actress could make a reputation at all."

De Varangeville blew cigar-smoke placidly. "Do you figure yourself that I am in the business to enable actors and actresses to make reputations? Flûte! Ah, mais non, mon ami, let us talk of something else! It is not such a cast-iron certainty, our play, that we can afford to produce it on philanthropic principles."

"In my case," returned Tricotrin angrily, "there is no question of philanthropy."

"Of infatuation, rather—hein?"

"Nor of infatuation, monsieur! Of devotion, I avow it, I avow it proudly—of a devotion sublime and eternal. But that in no way affects my judgment—it is a question of my artistic convictions. I speak simply as the author of the piece."

"Part author," said de Varangeville, with a quick frown, "part author, mon petit!"

"Bien, as part author! I accept the correction. As part author, then, I have pledged my word to mademoiselle Delacour that she shall create the part of 'Fifi,' and I must insist on her being engaged."

"Oh, really?" panted de Varangeville. He rose superbly, his arms folded across the heaving indignation of his breast. "You must 'insist'?"

"It is true!"

"Mon Dieu! I begin to awake to my insignificance; I do justice at last to the glory that our association would confer upon me." The satire in his rolling tones would have thrilled an audience at the Ambigu. "It is an essential condition of our affair that your little nothing-at-all shall queer the play? Understood! . . . Take it back, congenital idiot! It is yours; I shall survive without it." And, flinging the manuscript at the poet's feet, he waited like an outraged Jove to see him make a panic-stricken meal of humble pie.

This philistine did not comprehend the power of eternal devotion.

"It is like that?" rejoined Tricotrin loftily; and the gesture with which he met the outburst was no less splendid than his opponent's. "The price you set upon your service is my dishonour? For the boon you proffer, you ask me to be false to my vows—to abandon one dearer to me than life itself? It is to *me* you make this infamous proposal? Listen, monsieur de Varangeville! Were all the gold to which you hold the key amassed in one colossal heap in Brobdingnagian scales, it would not weigh with me against a single ringlet of her hair. I spurn your vision of a gilded shame. Poor in purse I may be, but I boast a wealth that transcends all percentages, all payments on account and in advance—the celestial treasure of a loyal woman's love."

The necessity for picking the manuscript up marred the dignity of his exit to a very slight extent.

If you were on the boulevard de Rochechouart,
not far from the rue des Martyrs, that New Year's
Day about 4.15 p.m., it is reaffirmed that you may
have seen a little lady, who was returning from a
rehearsal, exchange a careless bow with two young
gentlemen who were removing their household belongings in a hip bath. The young men were MM.
Gustave Tricotrin and Nicolas Pitou, and the lady
was——

"One of your ex-kindred souls!" observed the
composer. "At this date dare one inquire whether
that perfect union came to an end because she
could not be 'Fifi' at the Vaudeville?"

"Alas," said Tricotrin cheerfully, "it did not!
To have been banished from her presence with a
broken heart, after all I had renounced for her,
would have been dramatic and pleased me better.
We simply found each other tedious."

"And *La Feuillaison,* what has become of it?"

"I restored those three scenes to their original
beauty, and sent it round on my own. It met with
its twelfth rejection yesterday. Thirteen being an
undesirable number, I shall not try again. *But
the masterpiece that I am writing!* Ah, mon vieux
—the triumph that is in store! Congratulate
me!"

IX

A Reformed Character

AN attack of lumbago deterred a merchant of Rennes from taking a journey to Paris, and his sober-minded son said, "Mon père, it is I who will go in your stead."

"You? There are others who could arrange the little affair," objected his father.

"Others to whom the interests of the firm are so dear?" argued the young man, hurt. "Ah, listen, mon père! I know well that when I saw Paris last I was a feather-head, that I had artistic ideas the most deplorable; but all that is over—I am a reformed character, awake to the realities of life. Do not figure yourself that to return there would revive my bohemian errors! On the contrary, I shall rejoice more ardently than ever that I was influenced by your counsel and turned my eyes to the main chance."

"It was not precisely by my counsel that you were influenced," said his father, who had had to exercise stringent economic pressure.

Mariquot junior flushed. By now he had taken so kindly to commerce that reminders of his poetical period were unpalatable to him. As a rule

the dejected aspirants whom fate compels to
abandon dreams of renown in Paris for prosaic
callings in the provinces resign themselves slowly.
They submit, they have their luxuriant hair cut,
and they put aside their fantastic hats, but they
wail in secret long after the world believes them
sage. Some day you shall hear of a middle-aged
rogue of a moneylender who, unknown even to the
wife of his bosom, annually brought forth from
his safe a fantastic hat, to become, for an hour
again, a youthful idealist beneath it. Mariquot's
lamentations, however, had been brief. After three
months he had approached his humdrum duties
without acute disgust. When six months had
passed, the reflection that he was saving money
had given him a thrill of satisfaction. At the end
of a year he had strutted into the office briskly,
and spoken in pompous tones to the staff.

Little the staff surmised that their prematurely
staid young boss had once declaimed verses to the
stars and come within an ace of flinging himself
into the Seine! When the reformed character remembered how nearly he had been an exhibit in
the Morgue, instead of a future partner in a thriv-
ing business, his atrophic heart almost glowed
with gratitude to his preserver.

He got his way about going to Paris; and within
three days he had arranged the little affair with an
avarice that would have done credit to a riper age.
On the third evening, as he indulged in an appe-
tiser, with which he debited the firm, and thought

how inconvenient an appetite had been when he
was a poet, Mariquot again gave thanks that a
beneficent Providence had guided him to higher
things.

Now, on this evening there was at least one
other young man in Paris who viewed the profession of a poet as unprofitable. Never had Tricotrin seen less money in it. And never, at any
stage of their misadventures, had Pitou taken a
lower estimate of the financial promise of musical
composition. Moreover, their concierge's wearisome custom of demanding rent for their attic had
just reached a point at which they were compelled
to give it heed—she was going to turn them out
unless they paid by mid-day on the morrow.

When she had offensively delivered herself of
this ultimatum, and withdrawn, the pair sat gaz-
ing into vacancy, and so strained was the silence
that the ticking of their watches might have been
heard if those articles had not been in pawn.

Then Tricotrin sprang up and exclaimed, "I go
to throw myself at the landlord's!"

"At the landlord's—what?"

"Feet, of course, since you see me leap to my
own. In such a pass one must be economical even
of words. Happily, we know where his shop is!"

"I am with you!" proclaimed Pitou, rising too.

"No. If we failed together there would be no
more to be done; let us divide our forces. Your
turn will come if I am beaten. But hope for the
best, my comrade. A tout à l'heure!"

It was a close evening, with an autumn thirst in it, though the month was May, and everywhere syphons squirted melodiously. Striving to forget how dry his tongue was, and the temptation of the five sous in his pocket, the unfortunate young man hastened past the crowded terraces of the cafés, constructing his appeal. Street after street he traversed miserably until, having descended the rue de la Chaussée-d'Antin, he reached the window of an antiquity dealer, which bore the name of "Salabert." It was now nine o'clock and the shop was shut; but there was a private door. He had no scruples in infringing upon monsieur Salabert's leisure.

Scarcely had he pulled the bell when the door was opened—and by a maiden who might have stepped straight out of a canvas of Rossetti's. She faltered, "Oh!" It was evident that she had expected to see some one else. "I should offer no opposition to being he!" reflected the young man. And he said with the deepest deference, "A thousand pardons, mademoiselle. I regret infinitely to disturb you. May I ask if monsieur Salabert is at home?"

"Mais non, monsieur," she told him; "my father is out."

"Now how unlucky that is!" sighed Tricotrin.

She seemed to feel for his disappointment, and added gently, "He will be back at any moment, however—I thought it was my father who had rung."

"Oh, you thought it was your father?" exclaimed Tricotrin—and perhaps something in his voice betrayed pleasure that she hadn't thought it was a sweetheart, for on her lips flickered the suggestion of a smile.

"If your business is of importance, monsieur——?"

"It is of the highest importance, mademoiselle. Indeed, if I fail to see him this evening the consequences will be disastrous."

"Ah, excuse me a little moment, monsieur!" she said; "I will speak to my mother."

Next, a portly woman, in her evening black, advanced to him along the passage. "Enter, monsieur, I pray you," she said solicitously; "my husband will not be long. . . . If you will take a seat in the meantime?" And, somewhat embarrassed, he found himself nursing his hat in a corner of a diminutive salon obstructed by old bronze, and brass, and enamelled saints, amid which the mother and daughter sat repairing paled brocade.

"Clearly the shop is too small to hold all the stock," thought Tricotrin. "He has some nice stuff here." But he could not do justice to it for admiring the Rossetti profile of the girl.

"You had no appointment with my husband, monsieur, hein?" asked madame Salabert in an anxious voice. Dressed with the most scrupulous care, and with her hair done to perfection, the wife of the prosperous dealer was working by a bad light as hard as any sempstress.

"No, madame, no; my call is totally unforeseen."

"It is about some order that you wish to see him—there is something wrong?"

"Ah, have no misgiving, madame! My news will not take him aback," he stammered. And he began to debate whether it would not be wise to divulge his errand and enlist the ladies' sympathies before the antiquaire returned. Just as he was making a start to do so, the bell pealed sharply, and the girl ran to open the door again.

"He didn't take the key. How tiresome it is that one can't find a servant to sleep in, nowadays! I make no imputations, but I notice that among servants there is none who is either single or widowed. There must be a special dispensation of Providence for them!" rattled the woman at such a rate that no foreigner would have distinguished two words of what she said.

A parcel under his arm, as he bustled across the threshold, indicated that little monsieur Salabert had not been abroad on pleasure. His tenant was unknown to him by sight, and he viewed him apprehensively.

"This gentleman is waiting to see you, Edouard."

"Ah oui, on m'a dit. You desire, monsieur?"

"Monsieur," said Tricotrin, who had risen with a good deal of nervousness, "to begin with, I de-

sire to offer my apologies for presenting myself at
this hour. I am a poet, and not having attained
the income that is my due, I occupy a room on
the top floor of your premises in the rue Cauchois."

"Mais! Tildette, you are required in the
kitchen," said her mother, with a snort.

"Ah! It is monsieur Tricotrin?" exclaimed
the landlord, scowling.

"How gratifying that my name is known to
you! I do not exaggerate when I assert that in
the next generation, pilgrims will behold a memorial plate on the front of the house, announcing that I dwelt there. You are familiar with
my work, monsieur?"

"No. But I am familiar with your delays.
Bien! You have called to settle up. It was not
necessary—the sum should have been handed to
the concierge. Still, since I see you, I will take it
myself. Three-hundred-and-forty francs, n'est ce
pas? I will refer to my books."

"It was precisely on this subject that I wished
to make you an oral explanation," replied Tricotrin, stumbling forward to turn the door-knob for
the girl, whose shy glance betokened sympathy as
she retired. And then, undeterred by two protesting palms, he launched into a flood of eloquence so torrential that the little antiquaire,
hopping with impatience, had the greatest difficulty in stemming it. Not until a goodly part of

the peroration had been poured out could he contrive to do so.

"Listen!" he shouted. "I have nothing to subtract from the statement of the concierge. You pay, or you go. And you will not remove so much as a brush and comb."

"Well put!" said the lady warmly. "Do you figure yourself, young man, that monsieur Salabert invests in house property in order to provide the next generation with memorial plates? You had impudence to intrude here."

"Leniency for another month!" persisted the unhappy suppliant. "I ask no more."

"Too modest," said the landlord.

"It is unbelievable that you refuse!"

"However, it is a fact."

"Are you not human?"

"Yes; and your excuses would have soured a seraph."

His imperious gesture of banishment brooked no denial. Tricotrin tottered across the mat; and the swish of a hasty skirt seemed to hint that mademoiselle Tildette had been closer than the kitchen.

An optimistic temperament did not suffice to persuade him that Pitou was likely to fare any better. Lagging home, with his parched mouth, and defeat to communicate, his heart was like lead with an ache in it. The loungers on every café terrace that he passed now saw him waver more.

And at last, succumbing at the seventeenth, he dropped into a chair and moaned for beer.

It was when he had swallowed it and sat thinking how little of it there had been, that he noted that, at an adjacent table, a young stranger of moneyed aspect was regarding him with keen attention. "Can it be that we have met somewhere and he might stand me a drink?" thought the poet alertly.

At this juncture the gentleman leant forward, and performing a rite with his hat, remarked, "I ask your pardon, monsieur: do I deceive myself, or have I the pleasure of addressing monsieur Tricotrin?"

"You! My dear fellow! I am enchanted to come across you again," cried Tricotrin, wondering who on earth it was.

"We have met but once before, monsieur."

"None the less I rejoice to see you."

"You recall the circumstances of that meeting?"

"Some minor details may elude me, perhaps."

"My name is 'Mariquot,' monsieur," said the stranger impressively. "And you saved my life."

"A lunatic!" reflected Tricotrin. "But no matter; this should mean fluid in large quantities." He responded, with a wave of the hand, "Ah, you make too much of it, my dear Mariquot! Who *would* not incur danger to save a fellow creature from the tomb?"

"I shall refresh your memory," smiled Mariquot, who having done himself uncommonly well at dinner, with which he had also debited the firm, was in an expansive mood. "But first, we shall refresh the inner man, hein?" And when they had been supplied with whisky-and-soda, and straws, in accordance with the national belief that all foreign beverages are imbibed through straws, he went on, "It was quite a sensational episode in which you cut such a dash, and your features have remained stamped on my mind."

"Sad!" mused the poet. "But while he orders drinks, he may rave!"

"I am a business man, monsieur Tricotrin; and I do not hesitate to say that those who are in a position to judge would inform you that few men in the trade know more of it than I do. This may surprise you when you hear that as a boy I was absolutely idiotic."

"There we are! From his first years!" thought Tricotrin, grieved.

"I infer from your apparel that your walk of life is literary still? Well, not so long ago, I was a fellow victim. It is true. I lodged in the Montparnasse quarter. To the consternation of a worthy father, I was a poet. You will divine the intensity of his horror when I mention that, on the maternal side, my father was English. His tears and arguments were without avail; I steadily refused a position that offered prospects of the first order. And if he had not, finally, adopted a course of action that made resistance impossible,

I might have remained a scatter-brain to this day."

"You did—you might, I mean," assented Tricotrin, finishing his whisky-and-soda.

"Well, when I realised that I must indeed quit Paris," continued Mariquot, following his example, "I had to break the news to a young woman to whom I was attached. An actress." He toyed with his moustache, simpering. "She idolised me. As for me, the fact is I was already a little tired of it. But I was weak; and when I told her I must go, she made me scenes. Ah, mon Dieu, the scenes she made me! She entreated me not to leave her—she vowed that she would drown herself. She was distraught, positively distraught. I said, 'I do not wish to leave you; it rends my heart'—one must say such things!— 'but my father will not remit, and I cannot live without any money, voyons.' Figure yourself that she replied, 'Then die! My Love, let us drown together.' Ah, there is no doubt that I was all the world to her! . . . Let us have another veesky-soda. Garçon, sst! Encore deux veesky-sodas."

"And the ice!" said Tricotrin, his interest reviving.

"I repeat that I was weak—I was lacking in the force of character to say 'Not much!' Ostensibly I agreed to her plan, stipulating only that I should be too busy to execute it for a few days to come. My hope was that in the meantime her enthusiasm for it would abate. But if it did so, she concealed the fact with abominable cunning. Enfin, the evening arrived when—my whole nature protesting—we set forth together to hurl ourselves into the Seine. . . ."

"What a brute, that Salabert! We shan't be able to get another place, without any luggage; I don't know where a roof is to come from!" thought Tricotrin. "Your narrative enchains me," he put in politely, as the other paused.

"I need scarcely say that, with all the tact at my command, I strove, at this stage, to induce her to abjure our compact. Without admitting that I regretted it for my own sake, I spoke of the brilliant future that she was sacrificing; I mentioned that she would have been crowned with laurels, and diamond tiaras. The nearer we drew to the river, the more I dwelt on them. Moments there were when she seemed on the verge of acknowledging that she wanted to back out. But I realised by degrees that she was obstinately waiting for *me* to do so. Doubtless she had awakened by now to the fact that I had grown less enamoured of her; and in the fury of her wounded pride, she sought to thrust me into an ignominious position. I did not find that good enough. It was she who had originated the preposterous project—it should be she to sing small first. Stubbornly, she would not. What a pig-head! We reached the quay. As we stood waiting, with clasped hands, for our moment to die together, I hated her.''

The poet turned. ''He who talks interminably must say a good thing sometimes,'' he reflected.

''Fortunately, the scene was as yet too animated for our purpose; by a stroke of luck we had come too soon. So we wandered on—and happened on a humble café. And, having a franc in my pocket, I proposed that we should go in and sit down. I ordered bocks. The only other client was a romantic youth, who sat inditing a letter. . . . Does your memory begin to stir, monsieur?''

''Upon my word, I *have* some recollection!'' murmured Tricotrin.

''Scarcely had we taken a pull at the bocks than I discovered my franc to be a bad one. My companion, needless to say, had left her purse behind. In this predicament, which the insolence of the waiter made the more intolerable——''

''The youth came gallantly to the rescue!'' cried Tricotrin. ''Sapristi! so he did.''

''Justement. He approached with considerable elegance, and tossing down a coin——''

''It was a piece of a hundred sous.''

''He introduced himself, begging that we would consider ourselves his guests.''

''And a devilish pretty girl she was, I remember! We all talked for an hour or more.''

''*You* did so, monsieur. You talked eternally on some subject of personal interest to which I was too perturbed to attend.''

"Ah well, you have got back on me this evening," said Tricotrin. "Yes; I have a hazy notion that I announced the intent of committing suicide myself?"

"Possibly. I was not listening to you. The fact for which I have never ceased to be thankful is that your long-windedness had a charm for the lady. Or, more precisely, your presence tempted her to indulge that fury of wounded pride to which I have referred. She languished at you, with the design of convincing me that *I* was even less indispensable to *her* than was *she* to *me*."

"I do not read it that way. Her infatuation for me, if brief, was boundless."

"You deceive yourself. She had a tenderness for the very rug under my slippers."

"I also have my reminiscences, mon ami."

"But it is of no consequence. To-day I even forget her name."

"Her name? Her name was—— Now, what the dickens *was* her name? However, as you say, it is of no consequence."

"Her sheep's eyes at you, so far from incensing me as she intended, thrilled me to the core with joy—they provided a pretext for escape. I simulated an outburst of jealousy. I reproached her frantically for flirtation with another man in the very hour that I meant to destroy myself rather than bear life apart from her. Her remorse was frightful——"

"I do not seem to recall that."

"Of course it was frightful. You were a this-tledown, blown across her path, while I was her Here and Hereafter. She was about to say so. A moment more and she would have been on her knees. But I was gone!"

"And then," said Tricotrin, "she was on mine."

"As for that," said Mariquot irritably, "I don't doubt that, with feminine artfulness, she dissembled her dismay. The point is, that it was your garrulity that saved me, and I have always been conscious that I was greatly in your debt. Enfin, it would give me infinite satisfaction to seize this opportunity of repaying your service."

"*Comment?*" panted Tricotrin, leaping in the air.

"The question that I ask myself is, what form should my repayment take? The most helpful thing, if you had commercial capacity, would be to transplant you to a clerkship in my office——"

"Ah, no, no!" implored the poet wildly.

"But you have not. Very well then, I shall make you a gift. I shall give you money. It will not permanently improve your affairs, but there is nothing else to be done."

"Oh, my royal benefactor!" shrieked Tricotrin, nearly throwing himself on Mariquot's neck. "You little dream what your munificence means to me—what a tight corner I happen to be in! . . . Are you thinking of a tidy sum?"

Now, whiskey-and-soda, on top of the excellent

wine at dinner, was having its influence on Mariquot. He paddled in a wave of generosity. Or, to speak with more exactitude, he experienced a contemptible relish in parading to the gaunt eyes of a quondam colleague the disparity of their present positions. So he replied, in the tones of a multi-millionaire, "A few hundred more or less are of no importance to me. Let us say—a thousand francs. I have not so much about me, but I shall give it you at my hotel. Come there to-morrow morning. Here is the address."

"Oh, I have certainly tumbled into the columns of a serial!" thought the dizzied poet, stuffing the envelope into his pocket. "This is no longer real life; I am prepared for anything. In another moment I may be accused of his murder!" He was all agog to speed with the prodigious tidings to Pitou; and when a further quarter of an hour had passed, he thanked his stars to see Mariquot consult his watch.

"Well! . . . Remember that I expect you in the morning."

"Bien. No danger of my forgetting it."

"Say, eleven o'clock sharp. I leave Paris to-morrow. If you come at eleven, we shall have time for a little chat before I go."

"That will be superb. And I shall go to the station to see you off."

"That will be ravishing. Au revoir, mon cher Tricotrin."

"A demain, mon noble ami."

They parted effusively, and Tricotrin made for
home with such precipitance that at the foot of
the rue Lepic he nearly sent the stall of a vege-
table vendor flying. Pursued by her fluent com-
ments, he sprinted up the street, and mounted the
stairs to the attic three at a time.

"At last! Your clatter bespeaks victory. He
consents?" exclaimed Pitou.

"Consents? Who?" asked Tricotrin, mopping
his brow.

"Who? What do you mean by 'Who'? You
left here to see our landlord, didn't you?"

"Ah, so I did! To be sure! It had slipped my
mind. Well, I have incredible news for you, old
chap. Rejoice!"

"I feared you were finding him too much for
you. Eh bien? He says?"

"By way of welcome, he said I should have paid
the concierge. But he got ready to give me a
receipt."

"And then?"

"Then he gave me abuse, instead."

"Ah, zut! Stow it! Come to the point.
Finally?"

"Finally, he is a hog man."

"You mean it? You failed? . . . And it is on
that account I am expected to 'rejoice'? What are
you at? I believe you have been drinking spirits!
Answer me: how did you raise enough money?"

"Ah, censorious one! What will you? To
ᵔwn the truth, the obduracy of the hog man has

already faded from my thoughts. I no longer
recall the situation, 'save for one fair face, pure
as the image of some marble saint niched in
cathedral aisles.' *There* was my reward. I did
not stoop in vain. To be privileged to gaze upon
her was an ecstasy far transcending any financial
triumph.''

"You find it so?" cried Pitou wrathfully.
"Well, *I* did *not* gaze upon her, and I should have
preferred you to pull off the job that you went
to do.''

" 'Tis immaterial!" proclaimed Tricotrin with
operatic insouciance. "Instead, we shall toss him
his gold. What are a mere three-hundred-and-
forty francs? An adventure has befallen me—I
have saved a life; and at eleven to-morrow we
shall be rich. See, here is the unassailable proof
of it—an address! You shall go with me to collect
the treasure. I have only one regret—that I was
too dazed to touch him for a bit on account. We
would have cracked a bottle of the best now. Ah,
Pylades-Pitou, did you imagine I could play the
fool had I failed to rescue you? What agony that
you could misjudge me!''

"I did not, I did not imagine it!" asseverated
Pitou, embracing him.

"You did. And I should have been disappointed
if you hadn't. How inconsistent is human nature!
—a subject for a paper; I must write it one day.
Yes, the crisis is over. I have a most marvellous
recital for you. I have lived a whole installment

of a sensational romance since I went out. You
shall have it in detail, you shall hear it line by
line. Embrace me again, and lend me your
ears!"

Now, as always, it was a case of one purse between those two; and when the astonishing tale
was told, they pranced up and down the garret,
discussing what they would do with the balance
of the windfall after the rent was paid. The poet
spoke of an elaborate writing-table. The composer inclined to a fur overcoat. Both decided to
have their boots soled and heeled. It was an
unforgettable evening.

Meanwhile the expansive Mariquot had made
his way to a music hall on excellent terms with
himself. And it was not until the first dull turn
on the programme that it crossed his mind that he
had been unnecessarily lavish. His effect could
have been made with a smaller amount! Five
hundred would have met the case—why had he
said a "thousand"? He had been too impetuous!

Philosophically he dismissed the vexing
thought. But shortly afterwards it recurred; and
when he left the hall, the error chafed him all the
way to the hotel. Unlike Tricotrin, he mounted
the stairs in a state of depression.

Disrobing, he banished the matter formally
again. And a full hour had passed before he
realised that it had kept him wide-awake. At this
his blood boiled and he was enraged with Tricotrin. "Why should it not be five hundred, after

all?'' soliloquised Mariquot indignantly. "That is what I shall do—I shall give him five hundred! And he will be very well content." And soothed by the pleasing decision, he presently slept.

He awoke to congratulate himself upon it; and his satisfaction did not begin to subside till he was shaving. In shaving, the imminence of disbursing five hundred francs for nothing gradually elated him less. The decision looked pleasing no longer; he could not see what he had found in it to be so cheerful about. Five hundred was a lot of money!

"And for a veritable pauper, mind! One must remember his position; everything is relative,'' ruminated Mariquot, frowning in the mirror. "To such a fellow even two hundred and fifty would be substantial. . . . Upon my word, I shall make it two hundred and fifty! I shall give him lunch, and make it two hundred and fifty. It will be quite enough."

Thereupon he was cheerful once more. And his heart did not sink again till he began to count out the billets-de-banque that he was to part with. He fingered them reluctantly, and each of them was laid aside more slowly than its predecessor. . . . He sighed as he contemplated the total on the toilet table.

Punctually at eleven o'clock the two bohemians entered the hall of the hotel. It was with an air that the poet requested the dame at the desk to inform monsieur Mariquot that monsieur Tricotrin, accompanied by a friend, was inquiring for him.

"Monsieur Mariquot has gone, monsieur," she told him briskly.

"Gone?" croaked the poet, blanching to the lips.

"There is a letter for 'monsieur Tricotrin.'"

"Ah!" He snatched at it. It felt affrightingly thin. The envelope revealed a letter and nothing else. His panic-stricken rubbing and shaking of the stationery produced no bank-note! The young men clung to each other for support, and read:

"My dear Friend,

"It is with profound regret that I find myself compelled to depart by an earlier train.

"I have devoted to your affairs the most earnest, the most sympathetic consideration, and I see that to enrich you temporarily would be a mistaken kindness. The source of true happiness is labour. To youth a windfall is a misfortune in masquerade. If I sought no more than to take the facile attractive course I should joyously enclose herewith a handsome gift, but I recognise that to do so would be to clog the wheel of your energies, and I withstand the temptation. It is powerful, but I master it.

"Forward, my brave fellow! Advance always! I am convinced that you will realise later that to curb the baneful bestowing hand has required some heroism on my part; I am convinced that you will one day bless me for abstaining to indulge myself in a present delight at the expense of your future welfare.

"Receive in the meantime the assurances of my undiminishing affection, my inalienable interest in your career.

"X. M."

Speechless, they drooped from the hotel. Speechless, they crawled back, up the hill, to the garret. Both wondered, as they stared sightlessly into the sunshine, whether the prohibition to remove so much as a brush and comb would be enforced.

And then, what should be awaiting them but another letter—a line from the landlord, granting the month's respite that they had craved! A miracle had happened. Their tight throats relaxed emotionally; their nostrils quivered—the strained eyes gushed tears.

"Mon Dieu, mon Dieu!" cried Tricotrin. "It is astounding! There is but one thing to account for it—his angel daughter interceded for me! Nothing else can explain it. Oh, what bliss! All my crushing disappointment is forgotten."

"Ah, but no, mon vieux! That is going a bit too far; to that length I cannot accompany you," demurred the composer.

"Ah, understand me, I supplicate! I do not say that I have forgotten yours. The shattering of your own expectations I shall lament eternally; all my being is in crape for them. But as for myself, I repeat that the financial catastrophe has sunk to insignificance. Naturally! Tell me: if I may claim a ray of tender interest in a pure girl's heart, is not that a richer possession than the half of a thousand francs?"

"W-e-l-l—er—y-e-s—regarded from a literary point of view," said Pitou.

X

ANTIQUES AND AMORETTI

WHETHER Tricotrin's inference was correct, in attributing that reprieve to the mediation of his landlord's daughter, is a point that research has failed to determine. No authentic confirmation of his theory is known to exist. The circumstances, it must be confessed, lend some colour to the theory, but in examining the question the impartial reader will bear in mind the poet's deplorable propensity to construe any incident that befell him in the way most gratifying to his self-esteem. *Quot homines, tot sententiæ.* The intelligence of the reader will also intimate that the poet tied his best bow and flew to bless the landlord, with the object of seeing the girl again.

But she was not there. And Tricotrin wished much now that his garret were over the shop, that he might meet her frequently on the stairs. Every time that he took a little walk, his legs carried him worshipfully to the shop window, and though he did not dare to go in any more, he stood contemplating the display of antiques behind the plate glass till he could have catalogued them by heart. Alas! the Rossetti countenance of Tildette was never visible among her father's bric-à-brac.

One day, as he approached the window, he was greatly annoyed to see Didier spying and craning in front of it.

"Good afternoon, Didier," he said. "Are you in the act of choosing a present for me?"

"Ah! How goes it?" responded the painter with some embarrassment. "What alluring things, hein? Those ancient spoons please me inordinately."

"Me, too," assented Tricotrin. "But why did you pirouette on the tips of your toes to regard them?"

"Did I pirouette on the tips of my toes? Anyhow, why not? Is it bad manners to regard ancient spoons on the tips of one's toes?"

"You cannot be arrested for it. I simply wondered whether you were striving to examine something precious in the interior?"

"No, no," averred Didier carelessly; "the spoons, always the spoons! . . . Well, I must be off; I have much to do. See you soon, dear boy!"

"I also," said Tricotrin. "So long, old chap!" And they turned in opposite directions.

It was perhaps ten minutes later that, by a strange coincidence, the poet and the painter blundered into each other's arms on the same spot again.

"Tiens! Still the spoons?" cried Tricotrin angrily.

"Now is not this droll?" exclaimed Didier, affecting amusement. "You have hit it; they fascinate me! One cannot afford to collect such articles, but that is all the more reason for feasting one's gaze on them gratis. And you?"

"As for me, I was the prey of those old Chinese ivory chopsticks in a fish-skin case," explained the poet. And now who should come sneaking to the scene but a composer of the name of Vidlou!

It was evident that Vidlou was discomfited at beholding them there, and he forthwith professed to have been attracted by their presence. "Bonjour, you fellows," he faltered. "I was tearing along on the other side, and I recognised your backs."

"Jolly of you to cross over to greet us!" replied the pair with no enthusiasm. *"Quo vadis?"*

"Er—I have to call on somebody in the avenue de Malakoff," said Vidlou, obviously straining every muscle to see over the top of the curtain that screened the interior from view. "This appears to be an antiquity dealer's?"

"So it is. I had not remarked it," yawned Didier. "Well, we must not detain you, Vidlou. I myself have an appointment in a totally different district. What road is yours, Tricotrin?"

"Ma foi!" said Tricotrin, "I am rushing home; I have a man coming to see me, and I am late, so I must take leave of you both."

Whereupon the trio scattered, with a great show

of activity, each of them rejoicing at the departure of the others.

Now, not a quarter of an hour had elapsed when
the three young men, stealing back to the antiquaire's by various routes, converged under the
signboard and jumped dismayed.

"Mon Dieu!" began Didier confusedly. "Those
spoons——"

"Are too thin!" interrupted the poet, stamping.
"Do not seek to shelter yourself behind the
spoons, because they are inadequate. And our
friend Vidlou, who was bound for the avenue de
Malakoff? Felicitations, Vidlou! Sapristi! you
have accomplished the quickest journey on
record."

"Yes, what humbug!" agreed Didier passionately. "'The avenue de Malakoff'—and he is
here again in a quarter of an hour! Disgusting!"

"I fail to comprehend the tone?" said Vidlou,
taken back. "I am not aware why either of you
gentlemen should construe it as a personal affront
that I changed my mind about the avenue de
Malakoff?"

"Ah, come off it, Vidlou!" fumed Tricotrin.
"Your innocence is no go. 'This appears to be an
antiquity dealer's'! It is not to see antiquities
that you spend your life here with your nose glued
to the glass. It is to see nothing more antique
than a damsel of perhaps nineteen summers.
And the same remark applies to monsieur
Didier!"

"And then, monsieur Tricotrin?" retorted Didier, with folded arms. "On what grounds am I required to offer you justification for my attachments? I have yet to learn that you are either wedded or betrothed to the lady."

"Quite so!" said Vidlou, nodding. "Good for *you*, Didier! I concur."

"Do not presume to concur with anything I say —you are an odious rival!" exclaimed Didier at white heat. "It must be understood that your pretensions to the lady are to cease. My claim is indisputable, and I yield to no one."

"Your claim is indisputable? How is that?" rejoined Vidlou and Tricotrin together. And the former went on conciliatingly, "Come, come, we are comrades, we three; our friendship should be able to survive the situation. Do not let us quarrel! It is too painful, and it is also unnecessary. If one of us has indeed a right to bid the others retire, we may be sure that as men of honour we shall acknowledge the fact amicably—and you will both make way for me."

Much of this had touched the poet and the painter. "What Vidlou says is just, excepting the rotten conclusion," declared Tricotrin. "Very well, then, we will investigate the case. Didier first! Let us have particulars of his 'indisputable claim.'"

"When I say 'indisputable,' I would not have it understood to mean that I have any acquaintance with mademoiselle Salabert," said Didier;

"the courtship has not proceeded to such lengths as that. But it is fully a fortnight now since I lost my heart to her. She was dusting a shepherdess in that corner there, and I remained absolutely transfixed with emotion. A hundred times I have returned to the window in the hope of seeing her again. Further, I have painted her portrait from memory. Which of you dare boast of having painted her portrait?"

"Ah, my own experience was far more intimate!" broke in Vidlou. "I have seen something of the family, out of business hours. It was at a cinema; she was with her parents. Her face smote me during an interval. The effect on me was so tremendous that, when the entertainment was resumed, I sat unconscious of the screen. Do not ask me whether the pictures were comic, or blood-curdling, or educational. I know not. In the great darkness, which seemed as if it would never end, while I prayed feverishly for light, to behold her again, I realised that I had met my destiny. I realised that, when they left, I must follow this family—that I must discover her abode. Into a pastry-cook's, into an omnibus I followed them. I parted from them only when they had reached their door. And before I slept I had composed a serenade to her. Can either of you fellows pretend you have composed a serenade?"

"As I foresaw," exclaimed Tricotrin in triumph, "the hero of the contest is irrefutably I!

You will readily grasp the vast superiority of my own position towards the household when I inform you that I owe her father money. He is my landlord. I have exchanged some words with her in the sanctity of her home. I have the strongest suspicion that she begged the old 'un to show me clemency. More than that, I have written a beautiful poem about her. Have you two chaps the face to tell me that you have written a poem?"

His announcement that he had spoken to her was plainly poignant to the other lovers. But after a moment, Didier said in firm tones:

"While I do not deny that circumstances have favoured you so far, I cannot allow that the 'exchange of some words' constitutes an inalienable lien upon the lady's future."

"My view is not opposed to Didier's. Which I trust isn't offensive to him?" said Vidlou. "Moreover, since we are told that the exchange occurred within the walls of her home, we may assume that it occurred in her parents' presence and that the words were not passionate."

"Also I have exchanged words with her on that very step!" proclaimed Tricotrin, pointing proudly.

"Of a tender nature?"

"I do not say they were of a conspicuously tender nature; I inquired if Salabert was in, and she said he was out. But the fact remains that I have spoken to her. And her father is my very own landlord! There can be no question which of us is on the most familiar footing with the family."

"I uphold Didier's judgment," insisted Vidlou.

"It is idle to vaunt 'familiar footing' on the wrong side of a shop-window," said Didier, who was now accepting Vidlou as an ally. "It can impress no one. For myself, I am frank—I am outside because I can't go in. Simulating interest in the price of things, I have entered so often without spending a sou, that it is impossible for me to try it on any more."

"My own condition!" admitted Vidlou. "Just so. Before we can consent to withdraw on the strength of your familiarity with the family circle, my dear Tricotrin, we are entitled to demand a demonstration. All that is apparent in the meanwhile is that you are an exterior suitor, like ourselves."

At this taunt, Tricotrin haughtily expanded his chest; and a mighty impulse seized him to stride into the establishment forthwith. But he could think of no excuse for doing it. Since he was in monsieur Salabert's debt for the rent of the attic, he could not present himself as an intending purchaser of monsieur Salabert's antiques. His chest decreased, and he stood dumb.

His hesitation was not lost upon the others. Their lips curved in a fine smile.

"I agree with the last speaker," said Didier. "It is a practical suggestion. Come, demonstrate! In lieu of gaping at cups and saucers in front of a

velvet curtain, drop in and pass an agreeable half
hour. Vidlou and I will wait for you; we are not
in a hurry. There is a clock across the road—
we can time you by it. Look, it is a quarter to
four. We don't mind waiting till a quarter past!"

"Eh?" quavered Tricotrin, perspiring.

"Do you blench?"

"The test is not reasonable. It would be most
tactless to pay a prolonged visit to a prospective
father-in-law when he was absorbed in his trade.
It would be to give him a low opinion of my intelligence."

"You underrate your spell. As a favourite of
the family's you will be welcome. You may even
assist him to make a sale. Who knows?"

"I repeat that the test you propose is not reasonable," objected Tricotrin; "he is a busy man."
And an auto-taxi deposited two customers at the
door even as he spoke; a young, plump, rather
pretty woman, superbly dressed, carrying a be-
ribboned lap-dog under her arm; and a chic sylph-
like creature, who floated into the antiquaire's
on a puff of perfume. What language can do
justice to the poet's relief as he recognised in the
latter of these providential customers, his cousin,
madame Armel Duchambon, whom he had not beheld since his uncle assaulted him for aspiring to
her hand! "Nevertheless, since it actually appears that my veracity is in question and you
have had the bad taste to issue such a challenge,
I accept it!" he continued loftily.

Now, as the recognition had not been mutual—
as neither of the ladies had bowed to him—Didier
and Vidlou were miles from tumbling to the truth.
They looked at each other, startled, as he marched
with dignity into the shop and was lost to view.

"Bounce!" faltered Vidlou. "I give him three
minutes."

"Keep your eye on the clock. We'll rub it
in well!" assented Didier.

For an instant bewilderment clouded the beauty's brow as she found a shabby bohemian approaching her with assurance. But when he
asked, "Am I forgotten, my cousin?" she gave
a little captivating cry, and a smile that disclosed
dazzling teeth, and a dimple.

"What? Why, it's Cousin Gustave!"

"Himself! I saw you enter—and I could not
resist."

"Well, I should hope not! Mais vraiment!
I am enchanted to see you again after so long."
She turned gaily to her friend. "I discover one
of my family, voyez-vous! Permit me to present
my cousin: monsieur Tricotrin—madame Becquerel."

"Charmed, monsieur," said the plump lady,
while the little dog yapped. "Be quiet, Mees!
What wilt thou, my angel? Nobody will do thee
any harm."

"Very honoured, madame," murmured Tricotrin, bowing over his hat.

"Then I have not changed?" questioned the beauty.

"Yes; you are even more so!"

"Ah!" Her eyebrows swept the compliment aside, but her dimple approved it. "I am an old married woman, vous savez. Figure yourself that I have not seen this boy since I was affianced, ma chère! How culpable I am! I reproach myself. But, all the same, you know, my cousin, that I was ignorant of your address. I was not even sure whether you were in Paris, and——"

"I understand perfectly."

"You could have called on me, however. It was not necessary to wait for a gilt-edged invitation. I am furious that you did not call. As children weren't we playmates?"

"But afterwards you grew up!" sighed Tricotrin. "My aunt, my uncle, they are well?"

"Ah, oui, oui, ils se portent très bien."

Little monsieur Salabert had witnessed the fashionable woman's cordiality to his impecunious tenant open-mouthed. "Comment donc? Here is a pauper who is in a position to introduce valuable clients," ran his thoughts. "On ne sait jamais!" And he was so much engrossed by the scene that he started when the plump lady began to speak to him about a "Saint Sebastien."

Meanwhile the beauty and the poet continued their colloquy.

"My father was indisposed during the winter," she added. "Some médicament was recommended to him for obesity, and it did him harm in the stomach. But he is quite all right again now."

He wondered if she had ever been apprised of his brief matrimonial aspirations with regard to her. "I fear that I am never mentioned, hein?— I am still in their bad books? Answer me candidly, I beg it of you! Am I still a 'good for nothing'?"

She toyed with the tassels of her sunshade. "I avow to you that papa and mamma have always regretted your choice of a profession. Above all since——"

"Since I agreed to chuck it and then went back on my word? I understand. But your father, at least, was aware of the reason. I was not the weathercock that I may have appeared to you. If I could tell you how it has grieved me that I must have appeared to you a weathercock! Constantly I have lamented that. Listen——"

"But let us talk of pleasant things!"

"Permit me, I pray you, to make the explanation that has burnt in my breast! When I so eagerly consented to renounce my art in favour of shekels, it was because of a secret attachment that I must not allude to to-day. Commercial prosperity had no longer any bait to offer me when I discovered that you were betrothed to another."

"Mais—! What are you saying?" she remonstrated, pealing with laughter. "Is that the fashion in which you do not allude to subjects?

Don't be absurd. There was nothing too serious in that attachment, my cousin. You had seen me only once since I was confirmed.''

"Once did it!" sighed Tricotrin tragically.

"Ah, je t'en prie, Mees! What is the matter, my beloved? I implore thee be tranquil!" cried the plump lady to the lap-dog, which seemed on the verge of barking its ill-tempered little head off.

"Mamma and papa will be interested to hear that I have met you," resumed the beauty when the riot subsided.

"When you write to them I beg you will mention that they are always in my thoughts."

"I will not fail. . . . If I dare to say it, you have been a goose, my poor friend. I have no brother—papa used to regard you as a son. If you had only been amenable there would have been the most excellent prospects for you. It was always his desire, no less than mamma's, to establish you well in life. Certainly, when one is born a poet it is not an easy matter to devote one's energies to a business; I can understand your distaste; but it is not an easy matter, either, for a poet to make money—and money is a necessary thing, Gustave. You know that.''

"Even better than you, since you have never lacked it. So I appear to you an idiot, Henriette, and you lecture me?"

"I do not lecture, I have not the right; I simply advise. Because even now, perhaps, it is not too late.''

"Ah, you have thoroughly the right to say what you please! That point we need not discuss. I am honoured by your interest."

"Thank you; I am glad. And are you considering my advice, with that pensive air?"

"Chiefly I am considering whether to be lectured by you is painful, or delicious. It is a queer sensation. The little cousin has become a woman of the world, and the student of humanity feels like a child before her. Also when you look at me with that severe demeanour you are strangely beautiful."

"Wretched boy! you are hopeless," she rippled.

"One may worship, though hope is out of the question."

"Can you *never* be serious?"

"If I can never be serious—*I,* whose whole existence is a tragedy? Oh, you will not better that! Very well, we will talk profit and loss! Can you suppose I am unconscious of what a big thing I have missed by estranging your father and mother? Need I tell you that, again and again, I have said to myself precisely what *you* have said—and that I have said it with more forcible epithets? Oh, I know well that I have made an unpractical choice! I know that the day may come —that it is more than likely to come—when I shall look back upon the past, from a mountain peak of rejected manuscripts, with unavailing remorse. But what will you? The poet cannot change his

spots; I cannot re-create myself because I realise
that it would have been desirable to be made dif-
ferently in the first instance; I cannot re-write a
work of le bon Dieu because I see faults in His
construction.''

''You sell your manuscripts sometimes?'' she
asked wistfully.

''To be sure I do! What else have I got to buy
herrings with? I sell, though not at record prices,
nor so continuously that it becomes monotonous.
Ah! you must not pity me too much, my fashionable cousin; take me for all in all, I am a cheerful
idiot.''

''I must talk to madame Becquerel, I must
help her choose her things!'' she said. And they
joined her friend where Salabert was displaying,
with blandishments, a looking-glass that had been
the property of Louis XV.

''What do you think of it, monsieur?'' inquired
the plump lady, turning to Tricotrin.

''Topping, madame!'' exclaimed Tricotrin,
mindful of being in the dealer's debt.

''Observe that is of wood, monsieur, not plas-
ter,'' said Salabert deferentially, flipping the
carved gilded frame.

''And you assure me it is genuine Louis XV?''
asked madame Becquerel. ''Ah, hold thy tongue,
Mees! It is insupportable! I can endure no
more—thou drivest me to this extreme!'' She
tapped the demented animal delicately with the
tip of one gloved finger.

"Little dear! What intelligent eyes it has!"
said Tricotrin, who would have liked to apply his
whole hand hard. "Ah oui, madame, the epoch
is manifest by the carving—see the nest between
the birds!"

"Ah, you are a connoisseur, monsieur?"

"An artist, madame, that is all."

"My cousin is a poet," said Henriette, rather
as if he were celebrated.

"Mon Dieu! even her cousin!" commented Salabert to himself.

"A poet? Ah, what an ideal career!" gushed
madame Becquerel, lifting an enthralled gaze. "I
adore poetry."

"You have the air, madame," murmured the
scribe, trying to look as if he recognised a kindred soul.

"It was a present from Louis XV to his maître
d'hotel; I give a guarantee to that effect. It is
unique. At the price I have mentioned it is an
unheard-of bargain!" rhapsodised the antiquaire,
in an attitude of devotion before the glass.

"Bien! Send it to me," said madame Becquerel. "That and the 'Saint Sebastien.'"

"How she chucks it about! I do not buy a
postage stamp so carelessly," thought the poor
literary man.

"Au revoir," said Henriette, giving him her
hand, and her card. "You must take luncheon
with us on Sunday, you must make up for lost

time. Armel will be delighted to meet you. And we shall have a long talk.''

''I thank you infinitely.''

''Au revoir, monsieur. I hope I shall have the pleasure again,'' smiled madame Becquerel. ''We go, my ill-used pet, my little maltreated one. Ah, pardon the savage mistress that adores thee, ma Meesie, ma Fifi, mon toutou!''

For some second Tricotrin stood lost in reverie, while the penetrating protests of the little beast grew fainter in the distance. Then, awakening to the fact that Salabert was waiting for him to go, and that the half hour could not be up yet, he cast about him for a subject of conversation.

''How it enchants me to have had this opportunity of furthering your interests, monsieur!'' he said.

''Mon Dieu! Is he going to try to touch me for a commission?'' the dealer asked himself, aghast. And he replied with an air of ingenuous surprise, ''You consider your appreciation had any influence? I did not remark it, I!''

''No?''

''Frankly, no. I cannot say that I remarked it.''

''I regret. It would have entranced me to render you that gratuitous service.''

''Ah!'' The adjective melted his reserve. ''You are very amiable. Listen, monsieur. If, from time to time, you can indeed bring me any clients, it will not be a service that we shall enter

under the heading of 'gratuitous.' Reciprocity is
the soul of commerce, n'est ce pas? My motto is
'Always reciprocity.' "

"Good," said Tricotrin, as if he had battalions
of clients at his beck and call. "May I beg you
to do me the favour to glance, from the window,
at the clock across the road?"

"The time?" He pulled out his watch.

"By the clock across the road."

"Ten minutes past four," answered the dealer,
complying. "Why 'by the clock across the road'
particularly?"

"I have an appointment by the clock across the
road five minutes hence. A thousand thanks.
As we were saying, if by some unforeseen mischance, I should once more be a trifle late with the
rent, you will bear in mind that my friend bought
this costly glass?"

"Hold on! What?" objected Salabert. "One
must be accurate. Another motto of mine is 'Always accuracy.' No. I do not confuse my objects
d'art with my rents. Here I am antiquaire; there
I am landlord. The antiquaire is an artist, but
the landlord is a man of iron. Also the customer
was not your friend—you were introduced to her
in my presence."

"By my first cousin!"

"Your cousin, however, was not the lady who
spent the money."

"The brighter future for you—she has all the
more left to spend. Then it is understood? I

shall spread the fame of your establishment among all my swell acquaintances; and if I find myself in a further predicament, I may count on your sympathy as a fellow artist?"

"As an artist I should sympathise; but that would not help you. For I repeat that as a landlord I should be strictly business-like."

"You do not fancy that the artist might put in a plea for me with the landlord?"

"Not a word. They never meet."

"The landlord misses a fascinating companion. Would it be imposing on your good nature to entreat you to tell me how the clock across the road is going on?"

"Again? . . . It is just a quarter past. Do not forget that I have indicated a way to avoid further predicaments. Your commissions might be considerable."

"They might be," thought Tricotrin, "if it weren't impossible for me to find any customers!" And he answered, "You will see what you will see!" He opened the door wide, and turned with extended hands. "Au revoir, my good friend," he said loudly. "We must meet again soon." Salabert, responding to this effusiveness on the step, had no idea what a sensation they created. Didier and Vidlou could hardly credit their eyes.

"Gentlemen," drawled Tricotrin, rejoining them, "I trust the truthfulness of my statements is now above suspicion?" And, as the trio moved away, he added with chill politeness, "It may in-

terest you to learn that, impressed by my mercantile capacities, he seeks me for his partner and his
son-in-law."

"Oh, mon Dieu, mon Dieu!" wailed Didier.

"Hell and darkness!" groaned Vidlou. "Your
mercantile capacities? What does he know of
them?"

"I took Didier's tip—I made a sale for him."

"Miserable ass that I was!" cried Didier, smit-
ing his breast. "What did you sell, curse you?"

"I sold, for fifty thousand francs, an article
that he would have given away for firewood."

"Ah, go and eat firewood! What do you take
us for? Fifty thousand francs! That was all
you got for it? You are sure it wasn't any more?"

"Fifty thousand francs. Neither more nor less.
And for a thing that he looked upon as lumber.
I don't mind telling you that it was a broken
fiddle."

"He deals in fiddles?"

"It appears that it was part of an auction lot.
You will revoke the diet that you facetiously pre-
scribed when I mention that *I identified it as the
violin of Smith.*"

"Of what?"

"*Smith!* . . . You are not going to tell me you
never heard of the violin of Smith?"

"I cannot say I ever did."

"Where were you dragged up? The man with
this strange name was a violinist of England, who
had a devoted wife, called Pernelle. Pernelle

lived only for her husband, but the musician lived chiefly for his art. No one else has ever slaved at technique so inexorably as he; it was terrible to her sometimes to watch him, pale, gaunt, half famished, striving for mastery of the instrument that was to bring him fame. And the bitter years went by and the fame that he strove for did not come. And Pernelle knew why it did not come— she knew that there was no soul in his playing. And her heart broke at the sight of his despair.

"By her death-bed an irresistible impulse urged him to take up his violin again—and lo! the notes that issued from it were of such supernal tenderness that amazement stayed his hand. He seemed to be in the presence of a miracle. He played on. The attic and the dead woman on the bed were forgotten—he was lost in the grandeur and glory of the strains he evoked.

"Now the public and the critics marvelled at him. He was acclaimed the greatest violinist of all the ages. The world was at his feet. Bright eyes caressed him; white arms were eager to do so, too. But he had no thought to spare for love; the unparalleled triumphs of his art were enough. That is to say, they were enough until one night in Rome.

"Some instinct warned him against his passion. But it would not be denied, and he told her, 'I adore you. It is to *you*, Beloved, that I shall play to-night.'

"The house was thronged. The salvoes of wel-

come subsided. The multitude held their breath.
He drew his bow across the strings—and a ghastly
thing happened. There broke from the violin a
woman's frenzied sobs. It was as if an anguished
soul fled sobbing into space.

"When next he tried to play, he was again
mediocre."

"Is this one of the Tales of Hoffmann?" scoffed
Didier and Vidlou.

"No, it is not," said Tricotrin, with indignation.
"But you may bet your shirt that it would have
been, if Hoffmann had thought of it, instead of
me."

"And you pitched this yarn and sold a rotten
fiddle for fifty thousand francs?"

"No. But I might have done so if a fiddle had
been there."

"Morbleu! Explain yourself!" volleyed the
pair. "Are you to marry the girl, or are you
not?"

"I am not," affirmed the poet devoutly. "More
than that, I do not aspire to marry her—I shall
never marry; she whom I love is already a wife.
Ah, Henriette! Henriette! Pardon, my comrades, if I have disguised the aching love of a lifetime beneath a mask of levity! I withdraw from
the contest. It lies between you. Make the damsel your bride—either of you; I am unbiassed.
Whether she becomes madame Vidlou, or madame
Didier I shall toy but feebly with the wedding
breakfast."

The astonished and grateful young men nearly
wrung his hand off—and confronted each other
stiffly. With the retirement of the mutual enemy
they were allies no longer.

"Good day, monsieur Didier," sneered Vidlou,
with a formal salute.

"Good day, monsieur Vidlou," snarled Didier
with curling lip.

Not till a week later did it transpire—through
the servant at the antiquaire's—that the maiden
of the Rossetti face, whom a poet and a painter
and a composer had worshipped from afar, was
worshipping from afar on her own account—a
professional pugilist, whose prowess packed an
auditorium with the fair sex nightly.

"A pugilist? Ah, the new France!" gasped
the painter and the composer in an agony of humiliation—and even the poet was perturbed. "We
are back numbers with the modern maid, we artists. Upon my word, I do not know what France
is coming to!"

XI

WAITING FOR HENRIETTE

HENRIETTE DUCHAMBON said to her husband, "That cousin of mine! Figure thyself, chéri, that papa was eager to take him into the business—and the crazy boy preferred to write blank verse tragedies on a seventh floor! Tell me—thou art a lawyer and knowest the world—what can be done to assist a poet who has no common sense?" And her husband, the advocate, answered out of the depths of his wisdom, "Ma foi! one might invite him to dinner, my angel!"

"How stupid thou art!" pouted Henriette, throwing her powder-puff at him.

Then, taking tea with her friend, Simone Becquerel, she exclaimed, "Is it not extraordinary that a young man can be so stupid as my cousin Gustave? Figure yourself, ma chère—*etcetera.*" Whereat madame Becquerel, who was the romantic widow of a Deputé who had made an evil reputation and a pot of money, replied, "I cannot say I agree with you, my dear. Myself, I find such devotion to an ideal altogether charming. And it is thoroughly evident by his brow that monsieur Tricotrin has genius."

"Ah, flûte!" returned Henriette, pettishly, though she came near to kicking her ridiculous heels on the footstool with delight. And forthwith she conceived the lofty project of securing her cousin's future by marrying him to Simone Becquerel.

So it came about that Tricotrin, little dreaming that his beloved hostess planned to dispose of him to somebody else, met madame Becquerel in the urbane salon on the boulevard de Courcelles not infrequently. And in Montmartre they said, "Have a care, mon vieux! Poets should not be adipose till they are independent. Very noticeably you are putting on flesh!" Sheer envy, that, for the normal entertainment consisted of conversation, coffee, and cakes, with musical interludes on the semi-grand. But when they saw him sally forth in his best clothes and pictured him dipping into gratuitous dainties, the poor devils' mouths used to water. All except Pitou's, who was too loyal to allow it to do so. "Eat as much as you can collar, my comrade," he urged; "heaven knows you have many fasts to make up for!"

"Since I have confided in you, you are well aware that the fatal attraction that draws me to the boulevard de Courcelles is my cousin, and not her pastry!" said Tricotrin with a frown. "Could I summon sufficient fortitude, I would register a vow never to enter the place again." All the same, he was conscious that his love-lorn state had not prevented his doing the fullest justice to two square meals there; between the courses he had asked himself sadly, remembering a morning when her maiden presence had deprived him of the power of deglutition, "Can it be that I am growing old?"

"Commit no acts of renunciatory madness!" counselled Pitou with all the emphasis at his command. "For not only have you many fasts to make up for—you have doubtless many more to anticipate. Nourish yourself while it can be done, birdie. Besides, love is not injurious. On the contrary, experience has taught me that a devastating passion, providing it be sufficiently unrequited, is most beneficial to an artist."

"In that case, I am on the high road to be nominated for the Academy!" groaned the poet, cutting the colloquy short.

To give him his due, his devastating passion was very innocent; he sought no more that for Henriette to regard him sympathetically as a blighted being, one who had loved and lost her. But if he was alone with her in moments and seized the opportunity to heave a sigh, or start dramatically when she addressed him, it was not beneficial to hear her burst out laughing. Quite the reverse. Her laughter had frustrated more than one sonnet. He could not avoid perceiving that in some aspects her attitude compared unfavourably with her friend the widow's; indeed, he recognised that in other circumstances the plump widow, who was not more than three or four years his senior, might have made him deliciously unhappy, and he resented the perversity of a fate that had thrown a fashionable admiring woman across his path only at a juncture when he was incapable of falling in love with her. "In how many arid intervals of unattachment an acquaintance with her would have come to me as manna in the desert!" he mused bitterly.

However, being a literary artist, he put irrelevant thoughts like these aside. The thought on which he dwelt, with melancholy gratification, was that he had once proposed to make Henriette his wife and had his poverty thrown in his teeth. Atrocious! That her engagement to Duchambon had preceded any matrimonial intentions on his own part was another detail that he swept from his reveries. He had wished to wed her, and her father had laid violent hands on him when he proclaimed his tenderness! Intense indignation revived in his breast as he looked back upon the summary fashion in which his suit had been rejected. "Base, mercenary man," he soliloquised, "to sacrifice your child to Mammon! Did you debate which of us was her Affinity—did you for a single instant question whether it might not be the poor cousin who, in the long years before her, would prove the more capable of comprehending the requirements of her soul? Ah, no! Not you! And because the chastisement of conscience is an invention of the poets and novelists, I will not even tell myself that to-day you would give your life to undo your sin!"

Now, Henriette, who saw that it would be an enormous undertaking to marry a pauper to an affluent widow if he didn't co-operate in the effort for all he was worth, was eager to hammer practical precepts into him and train him in the way he should go. So, having met him near the flat one afternoon—she had been cashing a cheque to "Moi-même" at the branch of the Crédit Lyonnais—she took him home with her to *feeve o'clock* and a tête-à-tête.

"What were you doing here—were you coming to see me?" she inquired.

"No. I had only been sitting in the Parc Monceau, thinking of you and wishing you would ask me again."

"I half thought that Simone might come in this afternoon—I have not seen her for an age. By the way, I heard her tell you her 'day.' Have you called yet?"

"I went once, as in duty bound. These things do not interest me," he said.

"These things?"

"The small talk of smart women who belong to a Paris in which I am a foreigner—the spectacle of young men who spend more on gloves than I on rent."

"A propos there was some difficulty about the rent, n'est ce pas? As a relative I claim the right to repeat that it is not necessary for you to suffer too long or excrutiatingly in the matter, Gustave.''

"How sweet you are! But it is the landlord who suffers. And that matter will arrange itself —I have an offer for an old serial, from an editor who does not remember that he rejected it under another title. I thank you infinitely, though. You are compassion personified, in some respects. Mon Dieu! life is droll, hein? It used to be my dream to provide a home for *you*—and I live to hear you offer me the rent for *mine!*''

"Ah! Now, listen! No nonsense-talk! It must be understood that you are not to speak like that. I have a husband—and we are not in a play. Such bêtises do not flatter me; they do not even amuse me. Do not pay me empty compliments, but treat me as if I were a sister—and you will find me a very good sort.''

"Empty compliments! Ha ha! You know well whether they are empty. So? I am to feign forgetfulness. Bien! I submit to you in all things. But do not talk to me through your rue de la Paix hat, Henriette—do not, I entreat you, refer to the ache that I shall always carry in my breast as an 'empty compliment.' ''

"The ache that you will always carry in your breast!'' Her merriment was most embarrassing. "Poor anchorite, who has still to grow up! And when you are a man and get married yourself?''

"I cannot agree to your addressing me as if you were my grandmother; my 'sister' was bad enough," he remonstrated sulkily. "I shall never marry—never!"

"Then you will commit a very great error; I should be delighted to see you marry. It is just what you ought to do. Providing you don't marry some girl without a dot!" she added, as an after-thought.

"However, as I am not precisely a millionaire, I cannot anticipate ardent overtures from the parents of an heiress."

"There are wealthy women without parents," she yawned. "Simone finds you rather agreeable, doesn't she?"

"Madame Becquerel?" faltered Tricotrin. The immensity of the notion took his breath away. "You are not suggesting that I might marry madame Becquerel? What a madness!"

" 'Madness'? Why?"

"Why? For one thing, there is some disparity of position. And for another, I detest her dog. I could never write a line with that dog barking in the house all day."

"She might, for your sake, consent to board it out. Who knows? A woman in love will go to great lengths. But I mentioned Simone merely in passing—I daresay you will come across other women who could be the making of you. I may even be wrong in imagining that you could win Simone, if you tried—she has plenty of admirers; it might be no easy thing for a young man like you." She regarded him dubiously. "Your appearance is well enough, but I am not sure that you have sufficient personal magnetism.''

''I thank you for the testimonial.''

''But I may be wrong in that too. She is evidently taken with you—and she could afford to indulge a whim. In your place, I should call there, not once, but often. She is fond of poetry. Alors, seek her opinion of something you have written! And if, by a stroke of luck, she should comment unfavourably on a line, be enthusiastically grateful for her criticism. Then, when you have changed the line, you can go and read the new one. A poet reading his own work! It is attractive. There might even be veiled allusions to her in it. No woman could be insensible to the charm.''

''Henriette, when may I be permitted to come and read my poetry to you?'' asked Tricotrin mournfully. ''Ah, mon Dieu, this is the uttermost rim of the extreme edge of the limit! Impregnable to my homage yourself, you instruct me in the art of love-making for the conquest of another. Ignominy could no further go. Cease, I implore you! Are you without feelings?''

''My good boy——''

''Permettez! Once more, I was acquainted with you in your pinafores and your juvenility is no secret from me. It is idle for you, therefore, on the strength of having wedded my rival, to adopt towards me the tone of the Oldest Inhabitant.''

She accepted the correction with humility. ''I

was about to say that it is just because I have feelings, because I take an affectionate interest in your welfare that I put myself to the trouble of indicating to you which way the cat jumps."

"Much honoured. Too amiable! On my side, I reward your 'affectionate interest' with candour. I realise that the Henriette whose hand I sought in days gone by exists no more. Madame Duchambon has forgotten! But from the tablets of my own mind Time has failed to erase the memory of your early love——"

"*Comment?*" she cried. "I was never in love with you in my life! What are you talking about?"

"Well, then, *my* early love. And for the sake of what you used to be I shall remain constant to what you are."

"Gustave," she said sharply, "I have told you that I cannot have you talking to me in this strain! It is not gentil. Do not force me to rebuke you again."

"I apologise. I am penitent. But if you fathomed the depths of my emotions——"

"I do not wish to fathom them. I wish to hear nothing about them."

"You have but to command!"

"No; you have also to obey. Now, be sensible, je vous en prie, or you will make me seriously angry with you."

"That is all that is lacking—for you to hate me!" he groaned. "And yet, upon my word, I

am not certain but what I would rather have your
hate than your serene indifference.''

"Enough! you go too far.'' She stamped her
foot. "And I said nothing of 'hate'—one does
not hate children. But——''

"Jeer on! Mock me to your heart's content.
You have one?''

"But I shall not submit to a preposterous style
of address which I find an insult!''

"Ah, be just! An 'insult'!''

"I have been patient. I have tried to check
you. I have warned you again and again. You
are too silly to see that you offend me. Enfin,
I must speak plainly. If you cannot come here
without making yourself ridiculous, you deny me
the pleasure of receiving you.''

"So be it. You turn me from your door.'' He
took up his hat. "My humiliation is complete.
We shall never meet again.''

"We shall meet, I hope, when I can trust you
to behave properly.''

"We shall never meet again. Adieu, madame.''

"Bonjour, Gustave.''

"But I repeat——''

"I'd have bet my new frock to a sugar almond
that you couldn't get out of the room without turning round with a speech!'' she cried, exasperated.

"But I repeat that I shall be constant to the
end. When the pride of your youthful beauty is
no more—when the treacherous years have dulled
your remembrance of our farewell itself and old

age has bowed us both—you will know that up a staircase at Montmartre there dwells a feeble poet—that is to say, an infirm poet—who still recalls you fondly as you look to-day.''

And then he went, as enjoyably wretched as he had ever been in his sentimental career. And Henriette, who had really begun to feel sisterly towards him, yearned to box his ears for compelling her to forbid him the flat.

A week later, when madame Becquerel was to spend the evening there and inquired, ''And the cousin, monsieur Tricotrin, he will be present too?'' she yearned to box them again.

Since he had muffed his matrimonial prospect she regretted more than ever that his commercial chance had been lost. Was he always to be the family pickle, dreaming of fame and never attaining it? What an existence—in squalid lodgings, and perpetual danger of ejectment! She talked eloquently on the subject to her parents the next time they were in Paris—they were not staying with her because they disliked the spare room —and she painted an imaginary picture of his privations so pathetic that madame Rigaud's pince-nez needed to be taken off and wiped, and the silk manufacturer—after a vehement recital of all the wrongs that he had suffered at the poet's hands— said grumpily, ''Well, well, one does not desire to see him die of hunger, however. I may look the vagabond up. You shall give me his address.''

Thus, all unexpectedly, into the affairs of Gus-

tave Tricotrin did Opportunity enter anew. An
Opportunity unmerited and capable of extensive
developments. Having a lurking weakness for
him, despite his transgressions, monsieur Rigaud
took an auto-taxi to the Butte one morning with
more pleasure than he chose to admit. If his lips
were pursed, his eyes were soft. Once more he
was in the mood to let bygones be bygones. Once
more—after all the perversities of a headstrong
youth—it was conceivable that Fate might have
up her sleeve for the penniless poet a middle age
of prose and prosperity!

Monsieur Rigaud followed the directions of the
concierge, and tapped, exhausted at the door.

"My uncle!" ejaculated Tricotrin, in blank
astonishment. And drawing himself to his fullest
height he inquired sarcastically, "You have not
come to the wrong room?"

"Hein?" grunted the manufacturer, with a
scowl. "I have no acquaintance with anyone else
who resides in such a hole."

"Will you give yourself the trouble of entering?" Pitou was out, so it was possible for the
host to offer a chair without having to sit on a bed.
The cold courtesy with which he offered it was an
inadequate return even for the visitor's panting
perseverance with the stairs, and monsieur Rigaud, who had expected to see the magnanimity of
the visit emotionally recognised, was taken aback.

"Well?" he demanded. "What have you got
to say for yourself, hein?"

"I? What I have got to say? I wait to hear what has procured me the honour of the interview."

"Ah! It is like that?" exclaimed monsieur Rigaud, reddening with indignation. "What procured you the honour was the report that you lamented the error of your ways. By your demeanour it appears that the report gave you credit for more good sense than you can boast."

"My uncle," rejoined Tricotrin with immense dignity, "to err is human, and I lament various things. And, above all, I lament having submitted to the tyranny of your deed which wrecked my life."

"*Comment donc?*" He stared at him for quite a long while, striving to arrive at what he meant. "Wrecked your life? I was not aware that you had anything to reproach me with?"

"Ha, ha! . . . But it is superfluous to discuss your crime."

After a further ineffectual effort, the manufacturer said anxiously, "Listen, mon enfant! Try to understand that these are merely fancies; do not harp on them, and they will pass. We shall take you to a physician, who will put to rights very soon."

"Physician?" cried Tricotrin furiously. "Ah, c'est trop fort! He actually forgets!"

"But—name of a name!—what is it I forget?"

"My love for Henriette!"

"What? Silence, imbecile!" shouted monsieur

Rigaud, starting to his feet. "Your love for Henriette? How dare you say it? It is you who forget! You forget that your cousin is married now and such allusions are not seemly. Also your 'love'? It is a large label for that foolery of yours! The aberration that you have the audacity to recall to my mind was less serious than measles."

"Would you have called it 'measles' had I been a man of means? If I had been in possession of rentes, châteaux, automobiles, would your answer have been a blow? Ah, you wince!"

"A 'blow'? Zut! Do not exaggerate!"

"Yes, yes, yes, you gave me a blow in the chest! Make no illusions to yourself, my uncle. You condemned me to despair, not because you doubted my love, but because you disdained my position. . . . And you sleep sound at night, hein? Remorse does not rend you? What a world! It is the upright whom remorse afflicts—the worthy souls who have been betrayed into some venial fault; the malefactors are conscienceless and calm."

"I am not here to listen to your literary disquisitions!" roared monsieur Rigaud. "You may go to hell!"

"Positively you dwell content," resumed the poet, contemplating him with shrinking curiosity, "you who divided two kindred souls for life! What matters a nephew's desolation—what matter a daughter's tears? To glut your gaze upon her husband's income is enough—you are content! Purseproud and myopic, you see no deeper than your child's material welfare—the imperious longings of her heart are hidden from you!''

For all his ire, he had no black intention to deceive. That he conveyed a harrowingly false idea was due to his instinctive obedience to the laws of climacteric effect; he was the sport of his own oratory. But the agitated father stumbled down those stairs in the firm belief that Henriette was dying of love for her cousin; and next, madame Rigaud fell into the flat on the boulevard de Courcelles with her hat at the back of her head, gasping: "Ma petite, ma petite! Ah, what horror! Who could have foreseen that this fatal attachment would consume thee?"

And when Henriette had succeeded in convincing her parents that she was really very chirpy— which took a whole afternoon, because they kept crying, "But confide in us, we implore thee! Do not conceal thine agonies from thy mamma and papa!"—and then when she had induced her father to forego his design of revisiting the poet with a stick, she wrote such a note to the culprit— such a note!—that, too distraught even to pen her a last farewell, Tricotrin rushed headlong to the river, and stood there for fully a quarter of an hour, trying to think that he meant to throw himself in.

His reply to her on the morrow, beginning "You will marvel that I linger—it is because I

cannot destroy myself till you have pardoned me,''
would have filled two columns of *Le Temps*.

But it evoked no response. And though he
hung about a corner of her street until the concierges, and the agents de police in the vicinity
eyed him as a suspicious character, he never had
the luck to meet her.

It was when he had grown embarrassed by the
scrutiny of the concierges and agents de police
that he inaugurated the practice of seeking her at
madame Becquerel's.

Madame Becquerel, who had of course remarked
his sentiments for his cousin, had a shrewd idea
why he was never to be viewed partaking of coffee
and cakes in the flat any more—an idea in no wise
affected by Henriette's explanation that it was because she was "furious with him for having refused a definite offer of partnership from her
papa''; consequently the romantic lady was not
too dense now to divine the motive for his numerous visits to herself. When an opulent young
widow who has some claim to good looks and who
therefore thinks she is a Helen of Troy, conde-
scends to muse upon a bohemian in a morning
coat that is bright green in the sunshine she may,
not unreasonably, resent his frequenting her house
in the avenue Henry-Martin for the purpose of
meeting another woman. So, on one occasion, she
delicately popped the poet in a stew.

"One does not see you nowadays at Henriette's,
monsieur,'' she said sweetly. And then, to add to

his discomfiture, "I am sorry she never happens to drop in when you are here. It is unfortunate."

"*Comment,* madame?" He floundered, pink-faced. "I had not observed it."

"No? Tant mieux. I feared it must grieve you. . . . Might I trouble you to pass the chocolate creams for my little dog? She adores them. N'est ce pas, Mees?"

"You have heard, then?" faltered Tricotrin. "I was not aware."

"Ah oui. Henriette has confided in me." She meant him to understand that she had been told of his unreciprocated love, but when she had made him sufficiently uncomfortable, she was going to pretend to have been speaking of his adherence to his art. "What a tragedy for you that she should take it as she does! But you know, monsieur, frankly, many people would find your devotion incomprehensible. You do not mind my saying so?"

"Incomprehensible? That is to say, 'culpable'?"

"They would find it incomprehensible, too, many people. They would not be able to see where the fascination comes in."

"I am not of your opinion, madame," exclaimed the young man indignantly. "The fascination must be patent to all the world."

"Ah non! There are millions of persons who judge only by appearances."

"Mais, ma foi . . .!"

"And, in this case, you will admit that one must look below the surface to find the charm—it is certainly not the exterior that accounts for your choice. That is why you engage my interest—you do not mind features that would choke many men off."

"What?"

"It is rather fine of you. I said so to monsieur Duchambon."

"Du—Duch—*Comment?*"

"There you have one person who cannot comprehend the fascination. You are a mystery to him. He said to me, 'Honestly, I cannot make out what the attraction is'."

"He said that? He dared? Oh, mon Dieu, what a blackguardism! How did you reply?"

"I said, 'Tastes differ, mon ami. Monsieur Tricotrin has no objection to the things that repel you. He is an idealist. I admire him for it, myself. More, I am convinced that one day we shall see him triumph.'"

"You—you—— It was to Duchambon that you said this?"

"Quite pleasantly, of course—in a friendly way. . . . What is it? You are ill?"

"A slight attack of vertigo. It has passed. Yes? Well?"

Her malice was assuaged. "That is all. Personally, as I say, I admire your attitude; I find it beautiful that you choose the literary life despite its hardships, in preference to a partnership in

Lyons. I find it unjust of Henriette to be so angry with you about it.''

After he had fetched his breath, Tricotrin said, "Ah! I see my cousin has told you the whole story. Yes, she thinks it very ungrateful of me to refuse such a magnificent proposal from her father—and, after all, how *should* an advocate comprehend the ambitions of a poet? I rejoice to have your encouragement, madame.''

"It is a pity I am not a publisher!" sighed madame Becquerel, recovering all her gentleness. And she went on artfully, "Some afternoon when you come you are sure to meet her, and she will forgive you. You have only to come often enough.''

"How amiable you are! I shall not bore you?''

"Not beyond endurance," she smiled; "I am very strong.'' Mentally she moaned, "I am shamefully weak. But he is such a lovable baby, this boy!'' And Tricotrin, as transparent to her view as a shop window, reflected, "She is so simple-minded that I reproach myself for having to take her in!''

So, looking forward most faithfully to the afternoon when he would meet Henriette there, he went often to madame Becquerel's, and though the emotional afternoon was slow to arrive, he was bucked in rehearsing it. He pictured himself standing by the mantelpiece, the demeaned, yet constant lover. when she was announced—or he foresaw himself whitening to the lips as he crossed the threshold and beheld her. In either event it

would be apparent that her cruelty had shattered
him—and moved, she would yield him her hand.
Perhaps tact might accord him five minutes alone
with her? At any rate, there would be an opportunity to be snatched when she left. Before de-
parting for the avenue Henry-Martin, Tricotrin
used to study his aspect in the glass, and uncon-
sciously assumed a more woe-begone expression.

The anomaly was that he often forgot all about
it while he was there. It was easier to be constant in a bare garret, with a poor composer, than
in a luxurious salon with an attractive hostess.
Struggle as he would, his nature responded to the
variety and expensiveness of her clothes. "What
a sensational experience it must be," thought the
slum-dweller, "to embrace such a series of gowns
on a woman!" That thought would obtrude itself
into his most earnest discourse with her, and recur like an inapposite refrain.

Meanwhile Simone Becquerel recognised perfectly that she had supplanted Henriette, though
she didn't recognise how much the clothes had to
do with it.

One afternoon, she was posed on a couch, while
Tricotrin, at the uncomfortable end, sat recounting the history of his life. He had reached the
epoch of his sixteenth year, amid strenuous protests from the damnable lap-dog.

"I am sure you must have been a very good
son," murmured the lady.

"I believed so. But to be a good son one

ought first to be a father. When I have a son of
my own, no doubt he will reveal to me that I
wounded my father very often. Now I come to
think of it, that is a grave reason why I should
never marry—or why my boy should be named
'Nemesis.' ''

''You will marry, all the same,'' she laughed;
''and your boy will not be named 'Nemesis,' because your wife will think 'Apollo' more suit-
able.''

''No, madame, I shall never marry,'' said Tricotrin, recalling his fidelity to Henriette.

''Why not? To avoid the dissension about the
christening?''

He was silent. His insubordinate mind reit-
erated, ''To know but once the exultation of en-
folding such a toilette in one's arms! Would it
be feasible to clasp her ardently without damag-
ing the empiècement?''

''Why not?'' she said again.

''Because, madame, there is only one woman—
and she is unattainable,'' returned the poet, without being positive which woman he meant.

''Ah, what a misfortune! Married already?''

He tried to bow. But the toilette hypnotised
him. ''Can it be possible I am irresolute in my
affections?'' he asked himself incredulously. And
then, like one to whom a revelation has been
granted, ''Or was my sentiment for Henriette,
after all, no more than a youthful folly—is this
the love of my life?''

He leant nearer to the lady, and shook his head.

"Then why 'unattainable'?"

"Mountains are between us—the mountains of her gold."

"Love leaps mountains. If she loves you they will not keep her from you. Beyond them she will find a vaster treasure than gold—she will find happiness. Perhaps for the first time!"

"You think so? How pensively you say it!"

"I speak from sad experience. Betrothed as a mere child—what did I know of love, what has life yielded me? The world deems me content —I wear a smile—but I was meant for fine things. The frivolities by which you see me surrounded are no joys, believe me—they are but narcotics to a mind in pain." And she really thought so in moods like this.

"Poor girl! Ah, yes, I have seen you were solitary; from me you could not hide your nature. Constantly I have regretted that you were not poor, that you were not some humble midinette, that I might speak to you from my heart without danger of offence."

"Figure yourself that I am a midinette!" replied the widow softly. "It is not a salon we are in—it is a little room under the tiles. It is not a gown of Paquin's I have on—it is a little frock that I stitched with my own hands. Look how rough the needle made my finger!"

"Ah, you are exquisite!" gasped Tricotrin, smothering her hand with kisses. "And what a beautiful frock you have made! Midinette, I adore thee. See, through the attic window, that morsel of the Heavens—it is not more eternal than my love. Were I omnipotent! I'd thread the stars for thee to wear, dear—a girdle for my Sweet; I'd pluck the moon from out the sky, Love—a bauble at thy feet. Alas! I am mortal. I cannot give thee the firmament, ma Midinette adorée, but I beseech thee—give Paradise to *me!*"

"Ciel! how happy I am," breathed the romantic widow.

"Who answers?" demanded Tricotrin intensely.

"It is thy Midinette."

"The comedy is finished. I seek the woman behind the mountains."

"And her name?"

"Is 'Simone.' "

"It is Simone who speaks," she whispered. And they had barely time to jump apart as Henriette was shown in.

* * * * * * * * * *

"It is not that I doubt my devotion to her," he explained to his delighted cousin later; "clearly, we are affinities, she and I. But for weeks I have intended a scene of a totally different genre when you made your entrance—the situation is not the one I had constructed. If you can understand me, it is as a dramatist that I am a bit taken aback."

XII

ANTENUPTIAL

FROM Lyons, madame Rigaud wrote, "I am content to hear the great news of thee, my nephew. Thou hast done well indeed. I had the pleasure to meet thy future wife at Henriette's— she is a fine woman; and it is well known that Becquerel left a large fortune to her. How I felicitate thee! All thy days now thou wilt be rich, despite thine errors, whimsical one. Who would have predicted for thee such a grand position?

"To spare thee embarrassment I send five hundred francs, and a beautiful cornelian ring. Its intrinsic value is not perhaps enormous, but thou canst say to thy fiancée that is an heirloom. Be not reckless with the money. Display would be bad taste, since she comprehends that thou art not millionaire. Thou wilt repay the sum later. It comes from my own purse, for thine uncle remains incensed against thee and will give nothing. Nevertheless his heart of gold rejoices in privacy at thy good luck."

"Privacy! I should have preferred parade!" commented Tricotrin. "One cannot demonstrate limitless devotion with five hundred francs."

274

"What changes in you the affair has wrought
—already you speak of five hundred with dis-
dain!" said Pitou, an undercurrent of pathos in
his voice. "Mon Dieu, how rum a world: I live to
see you—marry!"

"If you would know abiding happiness, follow
my example! Never have I set you a better one.
'Matrimony' is a synonym for 'bliss.'"

"There are purists who differentiate. However,
you may be correct, although you have not tried
it yet."

"Do not jest on sacred subjects," begged Tricotrin earnestly. "That kind of cynicism jars on
me now. Yes, it is true that the affair has wrought
changes in me—I am ennobled; I recall my former
ego with wondering contempt. It is my intention
to remove from my manuscripts two epigrams
which I took months to polish. When I wrote
them, light had not been granted to me; my view
of life was narrow—I was not husband and
father."

"You are not husband or father now, so far as
I am aware."

"In spirit I am both. The revelation of it!
Only by marriage is the beatitude of love revealed.
Hitherto love was unknown to me—I had confused
the gas-jet with the sun and written in compara-
tive darkness. You imagine that *you* have known
love. Boy, you are deceived. You have been swin-
dled by a meretricious imitation. Marry, I charge
thee, marry! Every moment is transfigured. Ciel!

to bend over the cradle, beside the mother of one's babe. What ineffable emotion! When I work, to see her enter, our child laughing in her arms! 'Bonjour, mon p'tit mari'—'Bonjour, papa.' As a bachelor you cannot divine what it means. Often I am incapable of replying. My eyes fill; the pen falls from my hand. My art was ransacking the language for beautiful words—and in an instant I learned that the loveliest are 'mari' and 'papa.'"

"'Premature' is rather decent too!" said the composer. But there was no flippancy in his mood. "Ah, yes, the regenerating influence of matrimony is apparent even in advance—already you are uplifted to a plane so dazzling that I barely distinguish you! I wonder——" And he sighed.

"It is false!" cried Tricotrin. "How can you dare to assert that you wonder, when you know in every fibre of your being that our affection is immutable? We shall stick to each other to the end of our days, we two. When I am married, you will be no less at home in the avenue Henry-Martin than you are now in the rue Cauchois. Ma foi! with what content I shall watch ycu, as you dine on meat of the best quality, and the valet-de-chambre fills your glass. And sometimes, for a joke, we will go and feed at the Bel Avenir; I will put on my shabbiest jacket and we will pretend that nothing has changed with me."

Pitou embraced him, with many nods. But at

the back of his mind he thought, "It will be a
joke with tears in it." He began to perpend a
composition to be called "La Fête Pathétique."

The fact was that the impending severance gave
the musician the blues—and blues of a deeper dye
because he felt his dumps to be shameful. "A
fine Pylades I am!" the poor boy would say to
himself. "In lieu of exulting at the approach of
Orestes' magnificence, I weep at the vista of my
own desolation." Yet he could not avoid weeping.
Not even that tragedy of Tricotrin's resolve to
jilt his Muse for Henriette had been so bad to
bear, for then the blow and the wrench had been
sudden, and now the pain of parting was protracted. Moreover, Pitou had been presented to
madame Becquerel and was not sanguine of being
so much at home in the mansion. To some of the
crew, who were in high feather at their anticipation of an entrance into fashionable life, he had
said, "Do not bank on it! She is very amiable;
she told me she was enchanted to make my acquaintance; I passed a pleasant quarter-of-an-
hour at the house. But when I left, it was with
no conviction that she would wait breathless for
my return. She marries a bohemian, but she
promises herself to convert him. You make a
bloomer in supposing she marries bohemia."

And his perspicacity was not at fault. Already
madame Becquerel had reflected more than once
that a gang of indigent artists with unknown
names would be no asset to her salon. She had

even recognised with a frown that the name of her fiancé was unknown.

In the first flush of betrothal she had been reluctant to mention to him that his social circle struck her as imperfect; but some few weeks later, when the presentation of Pitou had been succeeded by the introduction of Lajeunie, and Didier, and Sanquereau, and it appeared that these were but the harbingers of a procession, she decided to broach the matter. It was July. She had renounced Deauville for her lover and sweltered in a strange Paris; she felt it to be doubly just that her lover should renounce something for her.

"How happy I am, Gustave!" she breathed one afternoon, with her head on his breast. "How radiant is the prospect!"

The engagement was a month old now, and strange to say, the poet had not been hearing salutations from his "wife and child" for quite a fortnight. Though he regularly reminded himself that he swam in ecstasy, he had actually fancied sometimes that he felt depressed. If he had not known that an occasional quaking was pure rapture, he might have taken it for a symptom of alarm. "Angel!" he responded.

"You will love me just as much when you are celebrated—when the world is at your feet? I shall never point to your success and say, 'There is my rival'?"

"What? How can you think such a thing?"

"I do not think it; I ask merely for the delight

of hearing your fine big 'What?' I dream of
your laurels all day. When we are married I shall
do better than dream of them—I shall begin to
pick. You will see! A wife who is intelligent can
do much. I shall not rest till I help thee into the
coat of an Academician. How well thou wilt look
in it!''

"Baby!" murmured Tricotrin, chucking a
chest.

"One may discover short cuts to literary fame,
n'est ce pas—there is a royal road?"

"Not a bit of it! Oh, no!"

"No?"

"That is to say, those who have arrived main-
tain that there isn't. Between ourselves, the
journey is shorter from the Bois than from the
Butte. For example, a comedy that is submitted
to a manager from a bedroom in Montmartre is
not so good as a comedy that is read to him in a
salon in the avenue Henry-Martin. There you
have one of the subtleties of dramatic art! It
shows the value of 'atmosphere.'"

"I prophesy that managers will find their way
to our salon. Editors too—the most prominent of
them. How I detest Montmartre when I think
what you have suffered there! I give thanks that
the phase is nearly over—I shall be glad when
there lag no reminders of it."

"What does that mean—'no reminders'?"
asked Tricotrin blankly. "One cannot inter one's
quartier. All my friends are of Montmartre."

"At present! But when the right people are your friends, you will have no use for the tribe there."

"Use? No, they cannot advance my career. But they will remain my friends. Naturally!"

"What a loyal nature you have! How I admire it!" she exclaimed. "I believe you are prepared to travel through life with that crowd clinging to your arms? But it would be to make our salon an Exhibition of Failures. It would be fatal. The right people do not thaw to a house where they find a circle of the small fry. I speak of what I know."

"But what are you saying? I don't understand. You wish me suddenly to throw them over? My pals?"

"Mais non—to throw them over suddenly. There is always the gradual and graceful way. One must use tact in these things. To throw them over suddenly would be sauvage. It would be like an Englishwoman that I know of, a madame Brown. For years she signed herself to a certain friend, 'Yours affectionately, Agnes.' Monsieur Brown, at the beginning, was nothing important—his name was 'Ferdinand'—but in time he distinguished himself and grew rich. 'Ferdinand Brown' became an eminent name in England. One day the lady wrote to her friend, 'We remove to Park Lane. It sounds very grand, but it is only a small house, *etcetera*,—Yours affectionately, Agnes.' It was her last letter but one. The

last, a few months later, was a formal acknowl-
edgment of a little customary gift, and she signed
it, 'Yours sincerely, Agnes Ferdinand Brown.' I
do not desire to see thee commit a sottise like that,
my dear.''

Tricotrin sat wide-eyed; and after a moment of
disquietude, he said hesitatingly—

"Don't think me ungrateful, Simone—all my
being responds to your solicitude; I am more than
proud to have inspired it. But to estrange myself from my friends by suave degrees would be
no easier to me than to drop them in the fashion
of madame Brown. The 'gradual and graceful'
way is as much beyond me as the other.''

"You think so because you are a man and have
never tried it. With a woman to show you how,
you will find it quite simple.''

"No!''

"Besides, there will really be nothing for you
to do; it is always the department of the wife. You
may even wonder sometimes how it came about;
so far from feeling culpable, you may question,
'How is it that I never see them any more?' And
if you do happen to run across them, you will ask,
in all sincerity, 'How is it that you never come?' ''

"But all my affections protest! There are
things that one does not forget; I have spent the
most impressionable years of my life up there—
I have formed ties there that are indestructible.
I cannot gather my friendships into a heap and

demolish them, the night before the wedding, like a litter of love-tokens from bygone flames.''

"You have many love-tokens to demolish?" she queried quickly.

"If I did not worship you, if I did not recognise you as the most noble of souls, I should answer, 'I have none.' But since to utter a falsehood to you would make my flesh creep, I answer candidly. Such things accumulate. I assure you, however, that when they form a little bonfire, it will take the normal course—there will be no tears to extinguish it, nor any sighs to fan its blaze. I shall see but one face in that fire—thine.''

She pigeon-holed his perversity for a future occasion, and they talked on more sentimental topics. But the opinions that she had expressed lingered disturbingly with the poet. Though he told himself that she had made her final reference to the subject, his statement did not convince him. Meeting with Sanquereau on the homeward walk, he paused and addressed him with such unusual tenderness that the mystified sculptor inquired if he was ill.

"Ill?"

"Your manner makes one think of another World.''

"I am profoundly happy," explained Tricotrin, enraged, "that is all.''

And as he continued his way, he mused, "What an idiot I was to dwell on those chance remarks of hers! She was wrong, and I told her she was wrong. Voilà tout. It is quite right, what people say—I have a mercurial temperament; but morbleu! to get such a hump about nothing. It was ridiculous. One can be very certain that no years of gilded misery are before me! Ha ha! There is no danger that I shall ever gaze out into that high class avenue wishing to heaven I could exchange it for the common boulevard de Rochechouart. The time does not approach when I shall steal from an oppressive mansion to embrace a crony on the sly. If I had any fear of such things this all-gone sensation in the stomach might be justified, but since no such misgivings enter my head for a single instant——" Here he was dismayed to find that he was weeping.

"Now, upon my word, I should like to know what I am weeping for!" he reflected indignantly. "I shall end in losing patience with that temperament. I am to espouse a fine woman, who does not ask better than to lavish her fortune on me, and I adore her—I have told myself so a thousand times; and yet there is within me—I cannot deny it—a kind of qualm which might be hastily defined as 'funk.' . . . Ah, Simone, thou who art all in all to me—or at any rate, more than anybody else —or anyhow immeasurably dearer than any other of thine own sex—pardon! It is the dolefulness of dusk, Beloved—it is only the dusk that dims my joy!"

Meanwhile madame Becquerel soliloquised, "I am living a beau roman, but . . . Ah well! nothing is perfect. The ideal, of course, would be for another subsidence at Montmartre to ingulf the whole district. N'est ce pas, Mees? Tell me, thou dost not consider thy little mistress imprudent? Thou dost not mock thyself of my idyll? Ah, do not disapprove me, ma Meesie, ma Fifi, mon toutou!''

The Duchambons came back from Paris-Plage soon afterwards; and calling upon his cousin, with whom he was now on capital terms, Tricotrin observed:

"Verily women are a queer compound! Mark Simone!''

"What has she done?''

"Well, she is spirituelle, hein? I pledge you my word she has romantic attributes——''

"You need not, since she is affianced to a young man without a sou, and frizzles here through the summer.''

"And yet she reveals in some respects a vein of worldliness that one would not expect to strike in her.''

"She has been bred in the world. All the better for you, my cousin! The more I think about the engagement the more it entrances me. It's superb.''

"Ah, there we agree. I simply remark, in passing, that Woman's disposition is different from Man's. It is a question whether Man will ever understand her.''

"What an original reflection! Do not forget to make a note of that."

"And whether she will ever understand Man. There you have another reflection—less flattering to her, so not presented to her twenty times in every novel; but no less true."

"The explanation of your 'remarks in passing' is, of course, that you and Simone have had a tiff? Much of a one?"

"Not even a tiff. But I confess that our views are not identical in all things. When we marry she would like me to inaugurate a holocaust of all my friendships, because the chaps are not yet famous. I said it was out of the question, and she did not persist—more than half an hour. But instinct warns me that the subject is to be continued. It may run for years. Ah, Henriette, be a good fellow! I need some one to talk to and to cheer me up; I cannot confide the matter to my chums themselves—it would be to insult them." And he was garrulous.

"I understand the way Simone looks at it, you know," she said at last; "I am not flabbergasted. No, no, no, don't excite yourself! I understand you, too."

"But I do not want impartiality—I want partisanship; I come to be sympathised with."

"Very well, yes, all right! I sympathise. But you must acknowledge there is some excuse for her—a very good excuse: she loves you, and is ambitious for you. She is eager to do everything to advance your interests—every mortal thing that her position permits. It is not a heinous offence. It is, on the contrary, very touching. As a poet you cannot be blind to its beauty? Take a cigarette.''

"What I wonder sometimes," he said diffidently, after a heavy pause, "is whether I am justified in accepting her undoubted sacrifices? You—you do not think I might prove my devotion best by releasing her?''

"*Comment?*" she screamed. "Not by any manner of means! What an idea!"

"Do not dismiss it too hastily. There may be more in it than meets the cursory view. If that is, indeed, my highest duty, I shall not shrink from it, though my heart may break.''

"But are you out of your mind? Whether the match was good enough for her was for *her* to judge. Even if you were mad enough to wish to release her, on what grounds could you do so? There is nothing for you to say.''

"You cannot think of anything?''

"For the best of all reasons!''

"A family council would not meet the case?" he suggested timorously.

"Gustave," she gasped, darting stern eyes, "do not tell me that you want to back out! I could not support the blow. It would be criminal.''

"Back out?" he whimpered. "How do you arrive at such a notion? Do I not pant to make her mine? It is true that I begin to recognise

that the marriage state will be a new and strange
life; I avoid the fault of contemplating marriage
from a frivolous standpoint—it is a very solemn
step; but do not mistake my manly gravity for
dishonour, Henriette! Why, even if I did desire
to commit such a scandalous act, I should be
ashamed to admit it to myself!''

"That part I believe," she said, studying him.
"Well, don't talk about it any more."

Ten minutes later, "Henriette disappoints me
—it is fortunate she did not become my wife!"
growled Tricotrin, as he returned to bohemia under an umbrella. And as he sat alone in the attic,
"Mon Dieu, how solitary I am! There is nothing
I want so much as to open my heart to Pitou—
and I cannot do it without planting a dagger in
his own. Ah, what do I say? 'Nothing I want so
much'? Heed me not, my bride to be! It is the
patter of the rain, Simone—it is only the rain that
damps desire!''

In keenest contrition, he determined that the
hour had arrived for the burnt offering; and
feeling purified by the thought, set about stripping
the room of as many of the ladies' photographs
in it as belonged to him. The number was respectable, if the ladies were not, and when he had
rummaged for the love-letters, and all the other
mementoes that he had preserved, he realised that
an empty grate was a drawback to destroying the
collection effectively.

It was no light undertaking to persuade the

astounded and contentious concierge that he had
need of a fire at the close of a day on which the
temperature had been tropical; but he wrung fuel
from her at last, and ultimately he made it blaze.

"Behold, Simone! I do not hesitate!" he said
firmly, bearing the collection to the hearth. "All
that remains of errors that I deplore—I reduce
them to ashes!" And having seized at random
a photograph of a damsel in a fluffy frock reclining on the sward, he would have hurled it into the
fire the very next instant if it had not been that
his hand was suddenly arrested by remembrance.

"All the same, it had charm, that error," he
conceded, viewing the portrait thoughtfully. "How
delicious a fête this recalls to me—what a roseate
dawn of illusion! Didn't you look a dream in that
white frock under the almond blossom? . . .
Done with! the folly is finished. Still, I won't
burn you first, little woman!" And he took another photograph instead.

"When all is said, you had qualities," he murmured, contemplating it. "When you weren't
in a temper, no one could be sweeter. And you
have nothing to reproach me with, hein?—you
could not expect copyright in me. To-day you
would not recognise me. I am reformed; I would
not revive our romance if I could. Nevertheless—
for the sake of one scene in particular—you shall
not be the first, ma belle!"

"Sapristi!" he exclaimed, apostrophising the
next that he snatched, "how you could make me

laugh, you! You were good company—you said good things. Where do you say them now? Yes, the epitaph is merited—*I was never dull with you.* . . . Over! I shall never laugh again—I am another and a better man. But for all that, you must not suffer first, my child!"

Impatiently leaving the whole heap of photographs to be disposed of later, he bent to the letters. "Regard, Simone! I am resolute!" he cried, casting an empty envelope into the flames. And beginning to read the missive that it had contained, he sighed: "Ma foi, how it takes me back! I did not foresee, the morning I received it, that this would be its fate! Adieu, little letter that I had prayed for through a sleepless night, that I pressed to my lips so passionately when you came! Your leaves bear my own kisses—and I burn you. What a cynic is Time!" Whereupon he laid the letter sacredly aside.

"Come, come," he went on, rousing himself from reverie, "at this rate of progress I shall not be through by the nuptial morn!" And now, in all probability, he would really have made a start but that he was interrupted.

"Ten thousand devils! A fire?" complained Pitou, who entered, to stand panting on the threshold. "The room is like a furnace. I fuse. It is the heat of Hades. But this is outrageous, a fire this weather! Are you off your head?"

"Be gentle with me—I have been discharging a melancholy task," said Tricotrin. "Yes, now you mention it, perspiration pours from me in pools. Open the window! Where have you been; anything fresh?"

"Not till it has been open longer. Well, yes, there *is* something fresh: I go to Chartres for two months."

"You go to Chartres? For two months?"

"Yes, I've had a letter. My mother reminds me that it is a very long time since they saw me. And my parents are not young, you know. I should not be likely to find any job worth while before September, and she wants to have me at home till then."

"You go to Chartres? How soon?"

"She suggested that I should go at once—she sends the fare—but I have written her to expect me the day after to-morrow. I did not like to part from you at five minutes' notice; much may have happened to you before I come back."

"It is true. . . . Yes, the heat is intolerable! I suffocate."

"The date for the wedding is not fixed yet?"

"Not yet. But you are right—much may happen in two months. . . . We shall dine substantially somewhere to-morrow, you and I!"

"That was my idea."

"And I shall not call on Simone to-morrow—I devote the day to you in its entirety. If we took a trip to Saint-Germain, or Saint-Cloud?"

"She would not be offended?"

"I shall send her a little note, explaining."

"Good. Let us go out, and you can write it at the café."

However, they did not take a trip to Saint-Germain, or Saint-Cloud, because in the morning the poet evinced a preference for remaining in the quartier; might it not be the last opportunity they would have to spend a whole day together there? "There are endroits that have meant a good deal to us in our time, and we have not clapped eyes on some of them for ages. We might make a little tour of them. It would be interesting?"

"You have struck it!" said Pitou. And starting with the rue des Trois Frères, they passed a leisurely forenoon, regarding bitter bygones that had grace in the flattering light of retrospection. A superior déjeuner at the Bel Avenir was prolonged till three o'clock; and a concert-apéritif entertained them till the hour for dinner.

"What a swagger repast!" they observed to each other at its conclusion, issuing from the Taverne de Paris, arm in arm. "How delectable a day!" And the prospect of a sprightly evening was still before them.

It was not until the sprightly evening was on its last legs that their cheerfulness waned. As they drifted up the rue Fontaine, the impending return to their room subdued them both; both thought, "We may never return to it together any more!" On the terrasse where they sought a respite, their bocks stood forgotten on the table, and they gazed

in silence at the garish scene to which a myriad
associations lent, to-night, factitious tenderness.
To their right, the crimson eyes of the Métro.
Across the road, the pink lamps of the Moulin
Rouge, not yet extinguished; the huddled little
bureau de tabac; the name of the Brasserie Cyrano
in transparent capitals on its awning. Typical
of their struggles, the long yellow loaves behind
the baker's window, and the hint of climbing
lights in the rue Lepic.

"I shall not see this so often in the future,
hein?" said Tricotrin dully.

"It will be no great loss. And you'll come
sometimes."

"To 'come' to Montmartre! It has a droll
sound. . . . The avenue Henry-Martin is a long
way off—rather out of it?"

"You'll soon shake down there."

"Oh, yes; one can get used to anything. I grieve
that you cannot be with me to the last, you know."

"Not more than I do! Afterwards I shall miss
you at every step. It is not the first time we say
'good-bye'; do you remember?"

"Yes. In those days I was an ass."

"But both of us were younger; it hurts more
now. I am selfish to say that, but——"

"No, no, you are not selfish; it is nice to hear.
That I shall be missed is good, because there is so
much that *I* am going to miss. . . . Nicolas, never
think that you are less to me, even if—Ah! how
shall I say it?—even if the years alienate us."

"Don't talk such rubbish! I have no misgiving —we are not made like that. You and I are loyal pals, if we are fickle sweethearts."

"My affection for you they cannot kill—I swear it. But the cruelties of Time are furtive; perhaps, unsuspected by myself, there will be in me superficial changes that make me foreign to you— that cause an estrangement that I lament, but have grown too old to understand. If that happens, do not turn your back on me—do not become Time's ally! Aid *me*. Bear in mind my appeal of to-night always, always! Strive against the aversion I create. Say to me, 'You take the wrong tone—you set my teeth on edge.' I shall bless you for the tip; my heart will leap to its deliverance; thou wilt requicken for me the friend that I mourned!"

"It is a vow."

"Never forget! . . . Do I go to the station with thee in the morning, Nicolas?"

"Is it thy choice?"

"Yes. Last time I could not bear to part from thee in a crowd; now I cannot bear to part from thee sooner than can be helped."

"I ache to speak of all I wish for thee in thy marriage, Gustave, but my throat gainsays me."

"An oration could not tell me more. . . . Well? I have no zest for the return, but the room will not come to us. Shall we?"

And next day, when he had stared after the receding train, when he walked lonesomely, blindly

back, he thought, "It is the first volume of my
life that has ended—and first things are best."

Conscience-stricken at his plaint, he drooped to
a bench. Overhead, a languid breeze murmured
among the debilitated boughs. "Ingrate! do
you then ignore your joyousness?" he groaned.
"Simone, my sweeter self, forgive that blas-
phemy! It is the wailing of the wind, my queen—
it is only the wind that howls regret!"

Now, it may be that Meesie, sa Fifi, son toutou
had failed to respond to the widow's petitions for
approval, or that Paris in the dead season had
got on her nerves; or it may be that, on hearing
particulars of her engagement, one or two acquaintances who were among the first to come
back, or the last to go away, had in her presence
lost control of their eyebrows. But for some
little time the lady also had wobbled in her mind.
Her fiancé's hieroglyphics announcing his intent
to neglect her for the companionship of the Pitou
person had not served to confirm her ardour; and
plaintive reproaches followed. She consented to
forgive the affront, but she did not contrive to
forget it. And she was a widow young enough
to have relatives who felt entitled to be offensive
"for her own good."

Moreover, his continued susceptibility to the
dusk, the rain, and the breeze may have told upon
his love-making. In any case, a day arrived
when, on her rose-tinted stationery with her mono-
gram in papier-maché, and in her most literary

French, she confessed to him that she had been mistaken in her heart. In the envelope she placed the cornelian ring.

It was maddening that he was admitted just after the confession had been sent. Shunning his embrace, she stood hampered by her reluctance to speak phrases that he was soon to read, and her consciousness that she could not rise to the occasion without them.

"What is it?" he faltered. "Why do you repulse me?"

"I have this moment written to you."

"What about?"

"Gustave——" She had urgent need of the first line of the letter.

"Speak, for heaven's sake! You terrify me."

"Gustave—— It is difficult. I—— What I have to say is, that I beg you to be generous; I am at your mercy."

"My mercy?"

"I must deal you a heavy blow."

"Mon Dieu!" he exclaimed. "You love me no more."

She passed a very costly handkerchief across her eyes. "I am at your mercy; I cannot defend myself—the heart is mysterious; I owe you the truth. I feel an exquisite friendship for you; ever and ever I shall watch your career zealously from afar, but——"

"But you love me no more!" His head was bowed, and he was silent for a long time. The pathos of the scene moved him very much. His own gaze was misty, too, though, by a strange anomaly, he felt capable of bearing the loss with vigour. "Do not weep," he said at last gently; "do not weep, Simone! You are not to blame."

"Ah, you are good! I shall never forgive myself."

"There is nothing for you to forgive, my dear. You were right and brave to tell me; I honour you for it. That I have failed to hold your love is not your unkindness—it is only my misfortune."

"Gustave! how noble you are. I feared your reproaches."

"*I* fear them, too—it is not so easy, after all, to aver that it is only my 'misfortune'; no doubt it is also my fault. The flower of your love was yielded to me, and I have let it die. There will be no death for my remorse."

"No, no, it is not true; you make me feel guiltier still! It was friendship always, Gustave; only, I was mistaken. You must not suffer a hell like that because a foolish woman did not understand herself."

"You mean it sweetly, but—— Never to have won your love—or to have lost it? Ah, leave me the illusion, and the hell—I choose the thought that once you loved me! You are weeping yet. You must not. To make those eyes red for *me!* Vouchsafe me one moment of authority, that I may 'forbid.' "

"I cannot keep tears back. Never have you spoken to me with so much tenderness!"

"Never perhaps have you been to me so dear. Who knows? The heart, as you have said, is a mystery. . . . Adieu, Simone. I wish for you a happier life than any parting speech could hint, so I will spare you the tiresomeness of listening to one. There, perhaps, is the most unselfish thing that I have done for any woman!"

And, sunk in melancholy on the tram, "It is only now that I appreciate her at her worth," he mused—"now that I have lost her!" That primary sense of vigour had fled, and sentiment overwhelmed him. His mind turned to Pitou, and he half thought of a hurried line to tell him what had happened; but in the knowledge that Pitou would be wholly gleeful at the tidings, his sensibilities shrank from such despatch. It seemed to him that henceforward there would be one grief that he must always bear alone—that, amid all their confidences, there must be one subject on which his comrade and he could never touch without restraint.

Averse from society, he sat brooding in the garret till midnight; and then, driven forth by hunger, supped taciturnly in the darkest corner of Le Lapin Agil'.

On the following day, a late post brought him an incoherent summons from his cousin, who wrote that she was "prostrated by what she had just heard"; but since her incoherence appeared to be more censorious than sympathetic, he did not go. He replied that he was too stricken to leave the house. And as he left it, in the pleasant eventide, to get a stamp at the tobacconist's, something of resignation was borne to him on the charm of the hour, something of endurance. He sauntered further. Gradually his pace quickened. Cheerfulness revived in him, and he rambled, humming.

As the moon swam up, the crooked quartier looked its tenderest. From afar, the fiddles of the Moulin de la Galette were mellowed to a madrigal. Each moment the scene wooed him with a deeper note, and cooed to him a sweeter covenant. "It is my Land, my Home!" he said. "How could I desert it?"

Even the grim attic had a smile for his return. It seemed to tell him, "Wayward child, you are forgiven!" He hung his hat on the door at peace.

Suddenly he swung his chair to the table, and scrawled:

"Such news! Nicolas, my brother, how happy I am! I'm to rough it with you still. Isn't that fine? . . ."

He looked up from the letter and laughed for joy.

"Isn't it fine?" he crowed.

THE END